Modelling and Beauty Care

Made Simple

The Made Simple series
has been created
especially for self-education
but can equally well
be used as
an aid to group study.
However complex the subject,
the reader is taken
step by step,
clearly and methodically,
through the course. Each volume
has been prepared by experts,
taking account of
modern educational requirements,
to ensure the most
effective way of
acquiring knowledge.

In the same series

Modelling and Beauty Care

Made Simple

Lucie Clayton

MADE SIMPLE
B O O K S

HEINEMANN : London

Made and Printed in Great Britain
by Richard Clay (The Chaucer Press), Ltd, Bungay, Suffolk
for the publishers William Heinemann Ltd,
10 Upper Grosvenor Street, London W1X 9PA
First edition 1985
Reprinted 1985

British Library Cataloguing in Publication Data

Clayton, Lucie
  Modelling and beauty care made simple.—
  (Made simple books, ISSN 0265–0541)
  1. Beauty, Personal
  I. Title   II. Series
  646.7′2′088042   RA778

ISBN 0–434–98591–0

Production: Mary Gibson
Drawings and cartoons: Derek Hazeldine Associates
Cover illustration: Roger Dearden

Glittering Prizes

Making modelling 'simple' is as daunting as making diplomacy simple, or law or journalism or any other complicated, enviable and exclusive activity, but it can be achieved. Readers may consider that the exclusiveness has been over-stressed, that many a young girl's dream will be broken by the reality of learning from these chapters that she has not the height, or the shape, or maybe just the flair for this seductive and, you may come to think, preposterous profession. And if any eyebrow be raised at the last adjective, what else can you fairly call a vocation which welcomes girls who don't need to be either educated or pretty (that is, pretty in the usual three-dimensional way), provided that they possess measurements which few doctors would recommend and features which, when translated into two dimensions, command favourable attention; which rewards some devoted workers with the wages of an assistant sales-girl and others, no more intelligent, with higher fees in a week than the Prime Minister earns in a year?

I am indeed open to the charge that for most girls I have made modelling not so much simple as impossible, and I must plead guilty because for most girls it *is* impossible. But they will learn, I hope, that fact of life less painfully from this volume than from any model-seeking advertisement, however beguiling. Balancing the disappointments, I hope that there will be some readers startled to discover that they precisely fit the magic formula—that maybe *they* could be successful models.

Of all the sad words of tongue or pen, the saddest are these: 'It might have been!' In other words, unless they come and ask someone who will tell them the truth about their prospects, they will never know.

The lady to whom I am most indebted for her inspired research in compiling this book is Vicci Bentley, Beauty Editor of *Woman's Journal*. I am grateful, too, to all her sources but especially to Jean Broke-Smith, Principal of Lucie Clayton School of Modelling, and the best authority in the world on 'the model walk'; to Susan Blackie, our Head of Movement; and to all the beauticians who serve both the School of Modelling and the Lucie Clayton Secretarial College.

Appropriately, near the end of this book is the section on the kind of work which trained or experienced models may find, if they are lucky—proof that the prizes indeed are glittering. But to travel hopefully *is* sometimes a better thing than to arrive. I believe that in the journeying through these chapters readers will gain more rewards, more laurels than any modelling job can offer. For the confidence a model needs is the same confidence that most young girls desire, and it can be acquired in the same way, by mastering the techniques that make a girl attractive, and that may be the most glittering prize of all.

LUCIE CLAYTON
168 Brompton Road
London SW3 1HW

Contents

1
That's Life

Every girl likes to read fashion magazines and imagine herself winsome and willowy, swathed in beautiful clothes, her soft shining hair the perfect frame for her pretty features. In other words, she'd love to be in the model's shoes!

Fashion models have a tremendous influence on women of all ages. They are seen in the best clothes and cosmetics and their hair always looks perfect. Everything looks good on them—and they look as if they could take on *anything*. They are the **trend-setters** who always seem as though they get the best out of life. It's hard to imagine them looking shabby or feeling down-trodden. They make you feel it would be wonderful to be like them.

Most girls, though, simply close their magazines with a sigh of resignation. It's all very well to dream, but when luck and looks were handed out, someone had to be at the back of that awfully long queue. The reality, they tell themselves, is just plain ordinary 'me'. What defeatists!

It would be totally unreal to imply that every girl has locked inside her the potential to become a model and all that's needed is gentle coaxing before it blossoms into consciousness. In fact, you will learn throughout the chapters in this book that a girl planning a modelling career has to possess specialist qualifications, both physically and psychologically. But every girl *can* and *should* make the most of herself—whatever she looks like and whatever walk of life she hails from and aims for. Adopting a **positive approach** to the way you tackle both your looks and your developing personality is one of the basic lessons a model has to learn—a lesson which is the foundation stone of success in any profession, from secretary to star!

In many respects, a model is just like any other attractive young woman. In fact, the skills which blend together, making her that paragon of completeness which her profession requires her to seem, are the basic ingredients which make up every young girl's life. Her knowledge of herself, her 'illusionist's' skill of hairstyling and make-up, her grace, poise and sense of co-ordination combine to give her the air of easy **confidence** which is the envy of so many 'shy violets' who just can't seem to conquer their fears. But don't think for a second that she hasn't had her own moments of extreme self-doubt. It's simply that she has learned to cope with and control them.

So how does a model acquire these skills and learn her trade? Although a formal training is not absolutely essential, many girls do begin with a **grooming course** at model school. Such a course not only helps a girl to get started in her career, by providing a good grounding to the modelling profession, but it also teaches her to build up the confidence so vital to a life which basically amounts to **self-projection** and **promotion** in both social and professional situations.

One of the worst nightmares a girl can experience is that of excruciating embarrassment through clumsy behaviour because she simply doesn't know the right thing to do. This feeling of helpless ignorance, which everyone suffers at some time or another, is a contributory factor to the inferiority complex which so totally undermines confidence. But on the other hand, both the **social know-how** and **self-awareness** which a model school develops in its pupils, combine to produce the happier, more assured personalities which have a head-start in any of life's roles.

Many of the girls who enrol for a grooming course have no illusions—or intentions—of becoming models. They may instead be planning a career in cordon bleu cookery, promotion, reception work or as top-class personal assistants to company executives. They may, of course, be heading for the top notches themselves! Whatever their goals, they find that the subjects covered—*the very subjects, in fact, which make up the backbone of this book*—are invaluable to them and their futures. Ask most girls who graduate from such a course what they have gained and, time after time, they will tell you that they have learned to make contact and mix with other people, co-ordinate their fashion sense, develop their own personal style and streamline their bodies and the way they move. (Even getting out of a car without flashing your all is an art form.) In short, they learn how to make the best possible impact. Just like models!

What schools cannot do is fabricate model material where none exists. In my own School we assess each model candidate before we allow her to enrol and we are frank to the knuckle about her potential. I know that sometimes this is sadly a crushing blow to secretly nurtured hopes. But it's kinder to tell her before rather than after.

During the training the analysis goes deeper. Students are sometimes shocked to see themselves on the video tapes which reveal the truth about the way they walk. Teachers have to speed the process of disillusionment and inevitably a few bubbles are burst. But the assessment is positive and slowly the girls learn that they too can master the techniques of elegance. It's rather like living a 'before and after' of the kind you often see in magazines—but on a much more practical and enduring basis. You learn how to make your shortcomings work. But if in fact a girl does have what it takes to go ahead and model, and she should be told before she embarks, a good school will bring it out.

Based on model school training, this book, then, is not concerned only with how to become a model. If you do in fact have secret ambitions towards a life in front of the camera or on the catwalk, the first and last few chapters will help you gauge your chances, and hopefully dispel any romantic notions you may have about the modelling business in general. But as everyone is 'on show' to some degree, I hope that all the subjects covered will not only fascinate but provide valuable references for a good-looking future.

Read and digest. With a bit of luck, you may never be the same again!

2
Have You Got What it Takes?

The world of modelling, the illusion goes, is essentially populated by beautiful people. A model is someone whom others admire—aspire to be like. To the outside world, she's one of the 'in' crowd—as near to perfection as they come. But not every girl with aspirations is going to make it. Modelling is a tough, sometimes ruthless business. The work is hard, the lifestyle often erratic and the competition tremendous. You're highly paid, sure enough. But to earn what seems to most people that extraordinary income, you must be a special breed of person.

A model's job is to make people want the kind of clothes she is wearing or the products she is advertising. In short, she has to **sell**, and if she doesn't succeed in selling then she doesn't stay long in modelling. But if she is successful, and *while* she is successful, she needs, if she is to stay sane, to develop qualities of character far beyond those normally given to the average pretty girl.

I know that you can't measure prettiness but let us presume that one adult girl in twenty is pretty—not just in her mother's eyes or her boyfriend's but in the steely-eyed view of a hard-nosed jury or, to put it another way, in the view of an advertising man or woman.

Next, the **measure test**, which can be passed only by girls whose height without shoes is within one inch of 5′ 8″ and whose other statistics are within a similar inch of 33″, 23″, 35″, or 173 cm height, and 84 cm, 59 cm, 89 cm. Less exalted fashion houses decree within an inch of 34″, 24″, 36″, or 87 cm, 61 cm, 91 cm, with the same height. But that's it—no less and no more. Shall we say, and I think we are sanguine,

Lauren Hutton—an Eileen Ford top international model

that one girl in eighteen would pass our measurement screen?

Let us presume next, and I am again being hopeful, that one pretty girl-with-acceptable-measurements in ten is photogenic. And—starry-eyed optimism once more—that one photogenic girl in five has the TV-personality or the print-personality (quite different from the girl you meet and talk to) to command the viewer's attention and to *sell*. Statistically, and I think accurately, I have just described one girl in eighteen thousand, i.e. one in 20 × 18 × 10 × 5!

If such success is more than a one-day wonder, or even a

ten-day triumph, imagine the stresses to which so rare a girl will be exposed. Photographers, account executives, fashion and beauty editors, marketing men, rival model agents will all be after her, as they say, businesswise. Half of those who were rude to her, or at best indifferent, on her way up will claim to have discovered her.

On a different level and one even more difficult to cope with she will suddenly be invested with an irresistible desirability by men whom she doesn't even know or want to know, especially if she comes to know them. But above all she will become, willy-nilly, an example.

The word 'model' has many meanings, including a copy of something else, but also a prototype, a paragon which other people copy. Models set fashions not only in clothes, hair and make-up but certainly in those three fields above all else. Aware or unaware of what they are doing, thousands of girls, possibly hundreds of thousands and perhaps even including you the reader, will be buying or adapting or just borrowing some new idea, or old idea revived, that was first launched by a model girl and which then 'took off'. It's true that the girl is manipulated, the merchandise is planted on her by an advertising agency or a journalist or TV commercial producer or public relations executive. In truth she is singing someone else's song but it's to her that you're listening and she stays in your mind when the song is over. They won't always know her name as they know the names of singers and film stars but across the country, and sometimes across the world, girls will identify with her and—by wearing the shoes, the nail varnish, the hair, the clothes, the make-up she wears—they will aim to look like her, or as near to her as their own limitations allow.

Of course many *wiser* young girls won't try to look like her. Her success will instead stimulate them to develop their own personalities, to achieve their own individual styles. Famous models generate 'clones' but they generate variants and opposites also, as in the design field. Laura Ashley has stimulated some designers to copy her but more just to think again, and to think more effectively. That is the result, which I may modestly call the Lucie Clayton effect, that we aim at in our School and which I hope you may gain from this book. Realistic readers won't expect to look like Jerry Hall or whoever is next year's top model. But given the measurements there's no reason why they shouldn't aim, in their own way, to look as good as her.

The measurements for modelling start high and, as we now sadly know, if you're not at least 5′ 7″ or 170 cm tall you can forget it. As **fashion photography** and **fashion shows**, for which the above measurements are necessary, are the 'bread and butter' work, providing the backbone of your income, if you're shorter, you'll miss out on a high proportion of work. The camera almost automatically makes you look shorter by a couple of inches and dumpier by around five pounds so that most young hopefuls are rejected by model school or model agency and given diet sheets, and the instruction to come back six months later and several inches trimmer.

Very rarely agencies make exceptions and take on girls of around 5′ 6″ or 168 cm, say, because they have marvellous faces for **beauty photography**. But these girls have to be unusual enough to attract sufficiently steady bookings and stay buoyant. They never 'show' because they would stick out like sore thumbs—or little fingers—amongst their more svelte catwalk colleagues. **Catalogue work**—another great mainstay and once a refuge for shorter models—is now also limited to tall girls for the same reason.

Every week, and sometimes almost every day, I have shorter girls and too often their mothers on their behalf pleading with me to accept them as trainee models, and the argument sounds sensible enough. The applicants are indeed *average* girls and surely, they cry, the public want to see the garments they might buy on average people such as them. Not so. The public only think they do—or so the employers say, and that means virtually *all* the employers of both photographic and fashion models. And since they are the ones with the power to decide, honest schools and honest agents restrict entry to the tall thinnies. Even to them there can never be a promise of employment but such girls have at least the right equipment.

Does your face fit?

It comes as a shock to hundreds of girls who are turned away every week from the top London school and agencies, when they find they're not quite as good-looking as they thought they were. The trouble is, good looks in the real world often fall short of the idealism of the modelling profession. Being pretty isn't enough. You have to look pretty exceptional from your photograph before you get beyond the receptionist at an agency. Even promising candidates may need adjustments.

A school or agency may refer you to a dermatologist to sort out your skin, a dentist to straighten your teeth or a cosmetic surgeon to remove moles or in some cases, straighten noses. Every detail will be scrutinised. Don't stand there hoping they won't notice that small something you're a touch sensitive about. They will: the modelling business does not recognise sensitivity. (As soon as you conquer yours, you're on the winning side.) What they are really looking for is flawless skin, regular features with well-spaced eyes, a small nose and a well-proportioned mouth with good, even teeth. Oddly enough, strong or stunning features aren't necessarily the most photogenic. Far from it—a successful model usually has fairly bland features which can act as a canvas for make-up. 'One-look' girls tend to be typecast quickly and that narrows down the scope for work.

Fashions in looks are constantly changing, too. If you thumb through a book on the history of fashion, you'll notice how model looks have gradually become less stereotyped and more casual during the past thirty years. The very sophisticated and quite hard look of the fifties, with the strong lips, powdered skin and heavily arched brows of the stunningly beautiful Fiona Campbell-Walter gave way to complete fantasy in the sixties with the Shrimpton look and then the Twiggy style—false lashes and dramatic use of eyeliner emphasising huge, soulful eyes against deathly pale lips. The next decade saw a warmer, more colourful look, blusher made a comeback and the 'natural' fashion glowed with corals and russets. Now in the eighties, make-up is down to its all-time minimum, with lighter textures for a fresh, bright look, almost American in its approach. Natural good looks are here again and their prime ingredient is an absolutely flawless skin!

The age of consent

The best age to begin your career is between sixteen and eighteen, when your looks are at their peak (glossy hair, clear line-free skin with no bags or shadows), your vitality and optimism are endless and you have the maximum time ahead of you in which to enjoy working. Modelling is a young profession, which seems to be getting younger. Some agencies, in fact, take on part-time girls who are still at school (with their parents' consent, of course) although the strain on their studies and still-developing perspective is tremendous, as you can imagine. Modelling can easily go to a very young girl's head—the last thing which should happen. But by the time you're twenty-one, it's getting late. Many agencies are reluctant to take on girls over that age as few models work past thirty and a large proportion give up before then, because close photographic work needs a face under twenty-six. Fashion show models (once known as mannequins) go on longer but generally ten years is considered a very decent innings in this business and callous though it may seem, it pays to think of the day you retire from the word go! Modelling is not the job you'll be doing forever, or even for a major part of your working life.

Check your personality

You have to be **determined** to be a successful model. That generally means nurturing a basic optimism and practising infinite patience. Your personality can make the difference between whether or not you're accepted by an agency and then later, whether you get jobs. So your general attitude

Leading model Renee Simonsen: Photo: Ron Capobianco; Make-up: Rumiko
Hirose; Hair: Phillip Apelbaum; Stylist: Evanglos Droulias

should be reflected in the way you look and act.

First impressions do count, so make your impact bright,
fresh, eager to show off your good looks in their best light.
Be cheerful—even though you're tired to death from slogging
around town with a heavy portfolio; or if you're thoroughly
cold and depressed, whilst sitting in front of a non-committal
fashion editor, who uninterestedly flicks through your

pictures without reaction, let alone a smile. Agencies look for girls who they think can cope with treatment like this and won't give up after a week of '**go-sees**' when it hits them that modelling isn't all glamour. This is where, say most of them, American models have the edge on English girls. They're 'chirpier', more persistent—downright pushy, even—as they chatter their way through their pictures, constantly flashing their perfectly aligned teeth. The 'hard sell' maybe—but it does seem to work. At least it gets them remembered, whereas a more reticent character who cowers in the woodwork won't make much of an impression. You have to sell yourself. The character you project is part of your 'act', so to speak; and if you can't promote yourself, why should anyone else? Don't be depressed either, as the days roll by without a booking. It can sometimes take a good few weeks until you get your first job—the most depressing and self-doubting weeks in your career. But suddenly, the work comes through. And the fun really starts.

Gaining experience

Modelling school will give you a good basic grounding in the tools of your trade: make-up, hairstyling and the model walk, especially the inimitable model dance. By plentiful use of closed-circuit television and video tapes modelling schools give you an excellent idea of how to react to the camera. Agencies also advise inexperienced girls about make-up and try to point them in the right direction, as well as arranging test shots with photographers. These help to build experience as well as a **portfolio** full of professional pictures which clients will wish to see, to judge how you can really look. It sometimes takes three to six months 'nursing' like this before an agency feels confident of a new girl, which is one reason why I would advise any intending model who can afford it to spend four concentrated weeks at a good model school before she enrols at an agency. But there are other considerations leading me to the same conclusion.

Although some of them *think* they do, most agents in truth

Model Anette Stai – and jewellery. Courtesy of *Vogue*. Mario Giaviano

don't know enough about how to train a model nor do they possess the very specialised staff needed; instructresses in hair management, deportment, dress sense, dance, etc. Moreover, if they do have all these special skills, how on earth can an even moderately successful agent find the time, which she should be spending on getting work for her well-established girls, to devote to an untried novice? In a parallel field, theatrical and TV agents don't try to teach acting. They usually send their discoveries, if they haven't already been there, to a good acting school. By contrast, however, I agree that it would be better to go directly to a good agency than to an inadequate model school.

The next problem is a 'toughie'. A good model school you will know by its reputation, by the numbers and experience of its staff, by the standard of the premises and also by the economic environment—by which I mean that if there are no jobs available in or near Wishing-in-the-Wold then the Global Modelling Academy at Wishing-in-the-Wold may not necessarily last the course, even if you do. However, the simplest measure of the honesty of a model school is the well known Groucho Marx test. He didn't wish to join the kind of club that would accept anyone like *him*. All model schools accept girls who want the training only for their own enjoyment. But if one accepts you *as a model*, leading you to think that this can be your career, and you know in your heart that it can't be because, for example, you're only 5′ 5″ or 165 cm, then you should avoid it as you'd avoid a stall selling five-pound notes for fivepence. But how do you recognise a good agency?

Agencies

Here you are entering a whole minefield. Many agents, but not all, tend to be discourteous and abrupt and in self-defence they claim that you'd be the same if *you* had to waste hours saying no to vain and unsuitable candidates. A touch of rudeness you must expect, although you may not forgive it, but there are other far worse hazards of the profession and these you will not accept.

First, let no one persuade you into paying an agency **entrance fee**, whatever form the fee assumes. It's true that agents like to see photographs so take with you all the clear big pictures you have, even amateur ones. Do not, however, fall for the 'Get Your Portfolio Here' advertisements that, too often, unsuccessful and sometimes useless photographers try to trap you with. The agent will judge from the pictures you show her or him if it's worth your having a professional set done, probably for about £50, by some young fashion photographer or a more established photographer's assistant. Don't be too disappointed if your first or even your second set of photographs fails to have your agent stunned into speechless admiration. But every session, added to what you learned about yourself in front of the TV cameras at model school, builds up to giving you the expertise that, with time, will pay off and with good luck will turn you into a model.

Beware, however, the 'agent' who persuades large fees out of you ostensibly for photography. Too often he's really the agent only for the photographer with whom he splits the fee. The BBC has exposed this particular racket but it still goes on. And probably, along with so many other swindles battering on the vanity of would-be models, it always will.

I know of only one way to avoid the minefield I have hinted at. Even if you possess the right measurements, when you spend money on photography there is still the possibility that you may be being 'conned'. But if you *haven't* got the right measurements, know then that it's not just a possibility. It's a dead certainty. **'Character' modelling** and **TV modelling** provide exceptions for shorties, fatties, oldies and even uglies, but these diversions, which may require you to be armed with a card from the actor's union, **Equity**, have in-built miniature minefields of their own and are outside the scope of this book.

Take care too when 'agents' ask you to subscribe to **model-casting directories**, **headsheets** and other brainwaves that may assist you but certainly won't harm *their* bank balances. Some of these promotions are in fact advisable but how will you ever know?

And how on earth will you know which agents are due to go bankrupt next? Not all the best agents subscribe, but even membership of the highly respectable **Association of London Model Agents** (AMA) is unfortunately no guarantee of solvency. They do not guarantee even the payment of each other's debts. Indeed, in the few months it has taken to write this book three of the major London agencies have gone bankrupt. Models are not 'employees' and have a low priority when it comes to distributing a bankrupt agent's assets. There is nothing that I know of in the constitution of AMA to stop a former bankrupt from being a member and no way of stopping even a famous member going bust next week without a whisper of a warning to the agency's models.

Model Shelly Hack illustrates the famous 'model walk' at its proudest

Dear reader, there is no way of knowing these things. I said that you are entering a minefield and you must be aware that this is so. There is no alternative, except to choose another profession (and perhaps another minefield). But you can use your common sense. You can ask endless questions but ask them only of people who ought to know the answers. Don't believe the advertisements, especially those that say 'Models Needed'. Mostly models are *not* needed since there are far too many already, although not at the top. You can go only by reputation—and by instinct. Be cautious, and above all, be lucky.

The first surprise for a lucky new girl who has just started with a photographic session or a show or two is, well, that she has at least started. During this time she'll be under the constant surveillance of her agent and her progress will be monitored. Real experience comes from a growing awareness of yourself. You can't learn all there is about modelling from a few sessions. In fact, you never do stop learning, as techniques and trends are constantly changing. You have to update yourself—analyse your pictures with the photographer and your agency, then work on your faults; know your best angles, have in your mind's eye exactly how you look with your various expressions which you've practised in front of the mirror at home.

When on a session, if a **make-up artist** and **hairdresser** have been booked, watch and learn from them and bombard them with questions so that you're improving your own technique for when you have to do it all yourself. You're privileged in that you're most likely to be working with the top people in their field—so profit from it. Try and learn as much as you can about **photographic techniques** and what is required of you—and your make-up, if you have to do it yourself—under different types of lighting and film speeds. Concentrate on the photographer's instructions. He is the one who is creating the picture and can see exactly how you look. Learn too from the other models, especially during shows. Listen to their hints and experiences, watch how they project themselves and generally glean tips from them to bring yourself up to their standards.

Do you like surprises?

If you're the type who likes a settled existence in familiar surroundings, the model's lifestyle will come as a shock. At first, you'll meet around half a dozen new faces daily and even when you're a seasoned model life won't be all 'regulars'. Furthermore, not only will you most likely be working at a different studio or location every day but you won't know where—or if—you're working until literally the day before. Agents blame clients for this lack of planning and clients have been known to blame agents for a lack of efficiency in telling the models. Your role is simply to be there, punctual, forgiving, calm and, above all, ready.

Home birds are in for another shock. Travelling is an essential part of modelling, whether it's to a location in Britain for a couple of days, or a couple of weeks halfway across the world, again at short notice. Be prepared for these long hauls abroad. Many English agencies have links with similar agencies overseas and consider experience in the international market invaluable as well as profitable. (Rates are much higher in New York, Paris, Munich and Milan.) Six months in Japan, for example, may not only ensure constant work at a good rate of pay, but could provide enough experience for a new girl to return to England a polished professional with a portfolio bulging with pictures. 'Exile' is also the answer if a girl has been 'over-exposed' in the UK and is losing popularity as a consequence. Six months away provides a breathing space and a fresh approach.

3
Common Sense

There's more to modelling than having the right measurements and looking attractive. You need the will not only to do your job well, keep your head firmly screwed on and survive, but to help your client succeed. For me that is the most vital quality of all: the genuine **desire to help**, the readiness to go beyond the boundaries of your immediate job—and today this is the rarest of all.

Professionalism is a word often used in the model business, but sadly only too frequently in the negative context of a girl who decidedly lacks it! It's a nebulous word, denoting a collection of ingredients, some of which I shall try to analyse. But fundamentally it implies a **sense of responsibility** not only to yourself, but to those you work with—a philosophy you can apply to all careers in all walks of life. As a model, though, more than most, you're a team member; you have the same commitment to the youngest of hairdressers' assistants as to the prestigious designer whose collection you're about to show off. Bear that in mind, and you'll reap the benefits—popularity and success but above all, other people's trust.

Be level-headed

When people in the business talk glowingly of a girl as being natural, they don't just mean fresh-faced. A pleasant, easy-going and unaffected personality always goes down so much better than a difficult self-opinionated attitude which puts everyone's back up. Just because you've an interview at a model agency (or any job, come to that) it doesn't mean they'll jump at the chance to get you on their books.

New girls complain bitterly how depressingly critical some agents can be. There's a strong chance you're not the most beautiful creature they've seen and acting as if you are won't impress them. Similarly, when an agency accepts you, remember you're one of many. The competition is tremendous and although part of modelling is learning to 'sell yourself', people get very bored with ego trippers.

Be patient

There is a side of modelling which other people don't see and which at first you'll experience the most. One of the hardest things for a new model to come to terms with is the indifference of the clients. Sometimes they see as many as fifty models or more in a single week. They also see a model as part of the picture, not as an individual—and that's tough on the ego.

Clients book models according to a sophisticated queuing system. If they want a girl for their job, they will ask her agency for a provisional or optional booking, i.e. one dependent on cancellation or on someone more suitable becoming available. Depending how far down the 'queue' you are, your 'option' may be first, second, third, and so on. Sometimes, it's even worth a client taking a fourth option as positions can change so much in a couple of days. The options at the top may be cancelled and a model can suddenly find herself with a day off. But that's life. Nothing is guaranteed and it's something you have to learn to account for both mentally and financially.

You'll also need patience when you *are* working. Photographic sessions aren't always the buzzing hives of creativity you'd imagine them to be. There's a lot of hanging around. Make-up and hair can take anything up to two or three hours if the client and photographer are constantly changing their minds, confusing everyone and generally jangling nerves. But you must never show your irritation. Even if you're cold,

(most studios are like barns), you're starving hungry (everyone's forgotten lunch) and your head is splitting (the lights
can sometimes get to you) you must remain cheerful and
polite. If you have any reasonable complaints take them to
your agency and to no one else.

A lot of models knit to pass the time when they're not
involved in other studio activity. Whereas reading books
tends to isolate you, knitting still allows you to join in and at
least look interested in what's going on. It also provides an
ice-breaking talking point, useful when you don't know a
soul.

When you actually get in front of the camera, the waiting
is still not quite over. The photographer may take scores of
trial runs with 'Polaroid' snaps, before everyone thinks
they've got the whole picture perfect enough to commit it to
the 'real' film.

Don't take it to heart when everyone else discusses and
analyses the way you look, as if you weren't there. At this
point, you're their creation, remember! Just keep cool and
ask how you can contribute. If you allow the situation to
upset you, you won't look good in the pictures. After all,
you need attractive shots for your portfolio. And you'll want
the client and the photographer to book you again.

Be punctual

Punctuality is of paramount importance in most jobs and
social situations. But in modelling, as much as in any other
business, **time is money**. People who waste time by being late
for assignments throw everyone else out of step. A model
should arrive at least fifteen minutes early for a job. 'On
time' is *late* in this business! Remember that you would expect
to be paid overtime if the session ran over and you had to
work late. So you have an obligation not to keep everyone
else hanging around at the start of the day. Be punctual for
auditions and 'go-sees' too. Your lateness could mean you
lose the job—miss your appointment and the client may not
have time to see you.

Make absolutely sure you've correctly taken down your instructions for a job. If in doubt, double-check with your agency. Work out your route the night before so that you don't waste time by 'getting lost' or cut it so fine that you have to waste money on a taxi and arrive flustered and confused. If your instructions are to arrive on the session with hair and make-up ready, allow enough time to do it all well before you leave. The best start to the day—and the best beauty treatment you can possibly give yourself—is an early bedtime the night before. So restrict your social life to the weekends if you want to appear clear-skinned, bright-eyed and fresh. And invest in a good alarm clock.

Be organised

As models need to be ready for anything at extremely short notice, make sure all your personal papers are in order, especially your **passport**. You could be flying to Paris in the morning. Your model bag too, should be all present, correct and the contents in good condition. A good idea is to keep your accessories in labelled plastic containers (food containers are light enough to carry around), so that you cut out all that fumbling around for the right pair of ear-rings, say, or *the* necklace which goes with *the* bracelet. Take your portfolio and spare **model cards** with you on every assignment— you never know who may pop in to the 'shoot'. Also, take everything you may ever need with you in your model bag. Never borrow!

Be presentable

The way you look is your own best advertisement. Often first impressions are the only ones, so you have to appear 'together'. This doesn't mean that you have to dress yourself up to the nines for every casting. It's often quite a relief not to wear all that make-up! Model agencies often suggest that your 'go-see' or **casting look** should be fresh, natural and bright, with the minimum of make-up and just a simple pair of trousers and a plain white top. This leaves the emphasis to the real you.

Be meticulous about your beauty treatments. Visit your hairdresser regularly to keep your hair well trimmed and in condition. At home, set aside an evening a week to 'de-fuzz' your legs and armpits (which must always be smooth) and do a manicure and pedicure. You should be good enough to photograph from top to toe at all times.

Be practical

Everyone has money problems, but models have special ones. It's extremely difficult to budget and manage your cash flow if it comes in irregular spurts. Models can earn a lot—but they never know when. The average annual income of a reasonably successful model can range from around £10,000 to £15,000 per annum. New girls may be lucky enough to gross £8,000 in their first year—a tidy sum for a seventeen-year-old. But you do need capital to start your career. First of all, you could have to wait up to three months to be paid for your first job, as many clients pay only on publication of the pictures. You also have to pay for your model card to be printed. A very basic card, with one picture only (usually called a 'flier' as it stands in until a more complete card is compiled) costs around £40 for 1,000. More complete cards can cost as much as £400.

You may also have to pay for your **test shots**—those very first professional pictures which you need for your card and your portfolio. Although the majority of tests are done in the evenings by mutual agreement with a photographer, model, make-up artist and hairdresser—all of whom want the pictures for experience and their own portfolios—it can take time to organise and finally get hold of the transparencies. So the short cut is to pay. Then, of course, you need to buy the portfolio itself. Any old folder won't do. Good presentation is a politeness which you owe your prospective clients. Models need a bespoke book with facilities for prints and

SUE
MOXLEY

RAY ELLIS

Premier MODEL AGENCY · 01-323 1221/2/3 · 21 GOODGE STREET · LONDON W1P 1FD · TELEX: 8952022 CTYTEL G

Height 5'7½	1:72 Grösse
Bust 34	86 Oberweite
Waist 24	61 Taille
Hips 34	86 Hüfte
Dress Size 10	36-38 Konfektion
Shoes 4½	37 Schuhe
Inseam 31	79 Schritt Innen
Outside Leg 41	104 Schritt Aussen
Hair Blonde	Blond Haare
Eyes Dark Brown	Dunkelbraun Augen

A PETER MARLOWE COMPOSITE © PRINTED IN LONDON TEL: 031-362 4516/6

Front and back of a model card

transparencies which display their work with a business-like aura. Then there are your fares, living expenses, a few new accessories. . . .

All in all, you need at least £200 to £300 worth of savings to see you through those first difficult weeks. I have already

stressed that the only thing you should *never* pay is a regis-
tration fee to an agency. Steer well clear of agencies who ask
you for money other than their **commission** on the fees you
earn.

When the cash finally begins to come through, it's your
responsibility to process it in all the correct channels. Technically, you're **self-employed** and responsible for paying your
own tax and social security. The agency will automatically
deduct its twenty per cent or so from your cheque. Most
agencies recommend you to get in touch with an accountant,
who will work it all out for you along with the tax relief
benefits (like make-up, clothing and travel allowances) for
which you are eligible.

It's up to you, though, to spread your earnings out. Fantastic sums they may seem but don't spend your cheques all
at once. Designer clothes and a lifestyle which goes with them
must wait until you are established. Even then, never forget
the future which inevitably will include the taxman.
Compared with your friends you may seem wealthy but of
course most of them will already have had their income tax
deducted. Your tax debts have still to be paid.

Behave!

There is a fair degree of unreality surrounding the modelling
world—the so-called glamour side. But you owe it to yourself
not to let it affect you adversely. If you become successful,
the temptations and social pressures are enormous. Things
beyond your reach suddenly become accessible. Drugs and
alcohol, for example are two very real pitfalls which seem
sophisticated fun at the time, but if abused can develop into
the kind of compulsion which limits both your modelling
and, more seriously, your natural life, as well as being the
quickest way of burning up your capital. Keep a rein on
your social life. Reserve parties and nightclubbing for weekends. No one can be bothered with a model who can't keep
awake, has a crippling hangover and looks like death warmed
up.

Never let your personal life interfere with your career. Rows with your boy-friend *have* to be blocked from your mind whilst you're working or you won't be able to concentrate. Besides, who wants miserable pictures? The client certainly won't—so don't expect sympathy there. Try not to make personal calls while you're working and don't receive them unless it's an emergency or from your agency. Nothing is as frustrating as a model who keeps disappearing.

Trips to **locations** carry their own code of conduct. Many a client has a bitter tale to tell of 'unprofessional' models, who ruin the entire shoot because of their bad behaviour. Trips can be a strain for everyone in several ways. First, you're with the same set of people for a week, ten days, maybe even two whole weeks. So you have to get on and avoid personality clashes every inch of the way. Secondly, there's a chance you'll be staying in a very nice hotel, in some exotic place, which serves wonderful food and the room service is all laid on. (That's advertising work for you!) But you must remember you're *not* on holiday: you're there to work. Limit your food and drink (bikinis don't look good over pot bellies!). Do not take advantage of the client's generosity by running up extra room service and bar bills. Be careful in the sun (you can't afford to burn) and go to bed at a reasonable time, preferably on your own, even if the client doesn't. Enjoy your job—but don't get carried away with it. It's *your* reputation that counts.

If you're the new Shrimpton they'll want you anyway. But just for a moment presuming that you're not, you can at least make sure that by being exceptionally reliable, unusually sensible and thoroughly pleasant everyone on that set or on that trip will want you back next time.

4
Confidence and the Model Smile

Confidence is knowing that you're doing things right and feeling comfortable doing them. You're in control and in tune with your surroundings. **Experience** is the greatest confidence builder. If you face a situation often enough, you're bound to lose your awe of it eventually, because you know what to expect and how to cope. But it's facing the unforeseen that presents the real problem, conquering that initial lost feeling which can't draw on experience to fish you out of the swamp of uncertainties.

How *do* you casually chat to someone you've never set eyes on before and don't appear to have much in common with? How *do* you react when you really don't know how everyone else will, and how, in fact, you're expected to yourself? Shyness is more than an uneasy feeling. In a society where communication is all-important, it's a social handicap which can trick you out of many opportunities. The only comfort is knowing you're not the first to have to get over it yourself. Far from it. Look, in fact at the Princess of Wales. When we first 'met' her, she was 'Shy Di', the gawky teenager who blushed at any given moment, chewed her necklace for comfort and hid behind her hair. By the time she married Prince Charles, she was an elegant, confident young woman with a style all of her own, used to posing for pictures with a confident toss of her famous hairstyle and a radiant smile any model would envy. That's professionalism for you. She *had* to do it—but it can't have been easy.

The key to confidence, then, is knowing how to **communicate**—pick up the threads and make contact. Your opening gambit, and your ally throughout, is your smile. At first, it's a mask. You force it up at the corners and will it to stay there. As long as it's on your face at least you *look* as if you know what you're doing and seem reasonably happy doing it. But given time it becomes so spontaneous, you can even laugh at your own inhibitions. Why did you worry? You fooled them all. . . .

The model smile

It goes without saying that you see more pictures of smiling models than the shy variety that hide behind their hair. For models, the rule of communication is especially important—it's their very trade. A model's smile has to say so many more things than simply 'I'm okay'. It has to communicate whatever she's wearing and look as if she really loves every last detail. But here's the catch. If the expression doesn't come from inside—if her eyes aren't smiling too—the whole thing looks hopelessly false and falls apart.

Obviously, it helps if you're a jolly type of person with a healthy sense of humour. You'll find that as smiling is second nature to you, you'll have an instant advantage over any situation. But the average girl has to use her imagination more to conquer her inhibitions—the worst of which is actually looking *at* someone. Most people do anything to avoid eye contact. They'll stare at the other person's feet, arms, over their shoulder—anything but right into their face. At our Model School we use a very effective exercise to teach the girls to communicate. When they practise their walk and model turns, they begin by standing either in a circle or in two facing lines, so that when they come together at the centre, they can't avoid smiling at their opposite number.

Later, when a model is being photographed, she learns to look the camera in the eye. Watching experienced models work is like being a fly on the wall to an outrageously flirtatious affair. The model and the camera have a special relationship, where looks say it all.

But back to business, a model has to be something of an actress. She has to work a confidence trick on herself before

International agent Eileen Ford's Cheryl Tiegs illustrates the model smile

she convinces everyone else that she's really enjoying the mood of the pictures, letting her expressions describe how marvellous the clothes feel, too. Obviously, you feel different in a pair of jeans and a jacket from the way you feel in a ballgown. A model has to act those feelings—jaunty and casual for the one with hands on hips and head back laughing, say, as if she's out for a country ramble; serene for the other, head up, dignified and very feminine. Unless—and it happens—the photographer tells her to do exactly the opposite.

The textures for the garments have to be matched by your smile. For example, silk is smooth, slinky, so normally a sensual smile is more in keeping than a fully fledged grin. But it isn't always easy to look enraptured. A lot of the time, you're having to do things you don't actually want to do. It's lovely when you *do* like the way you've been styled, but in reality, you're only that lucky around a quarter of the time. Your daily duty is more likely to be making someone's perfectly hideous knitting pattern come alive; wearing a colour you wouldn't be seen cleaning the flat in; or sporting a hairstyle you're convinced makes you look a good ten years older!

Neither is it easy to snuggle cosily into a fur coat and hug a chunky sweater to you on a sweltering August day. Thinking blissfully warm thoughts as you bask luxuriantly in your bikini on the Canvey Sands in January also taxes your sense of ingenuity. The magazine and advertising industry works anything up to six months ahead, so you're constantly out of step with the seasons.

Studio work has its pitfalls, too. Studios are generally cold places to work in and lacking in atmosphere. You could be working in a draughty converted wharf or a leaking attic at the top of a warehouse. (It takes time for photographers as well as models to become successful. Only the top boys can afford scrubbed pine floors and central heating.) If you don't have props or accessories that you can relate to and make a feature of, acting in front of a blank white background can sap your enthusiasm. Then there's the way you feel personally. You may have 'flu coming on, your cat has just died and to cap it all, your tax bill came this morning. Then it really requires mind over matter! Think of the money if all else fails.

Shows are easier to perform with panache. For one thing, there are several of you in the same boat, you've usually rehearsed your walk together and there's the music to carry you through and keep you in the swing. Oddly enough, the sea of people in the audience isn't as off-putting as you might think. Sometimes the lights are so strong, you may not even be able to see beyond the first two rows. But an old model trick is to fix on one face in the audience and 'play' to it, every time you're on the catwalk. It will give you a much more lively expressive look than if you're blankly staring into nothingness. And of course in shows the famous model smile gets cooler as the clothes become more expensive. Indeed, in the Paris collections I've seen all the models looking absolutely furious. But don't try it in your first job or two.

Finally, a golden rule which appears on a model agency list of do's and don'ts for their new girls. It also has a definite universal appeal: 'Never apologise for lack of experience. Unless you tell them, they may never know!'

The cheerful approach

Models are the talking point, the centre of this book. But the advice which, with the aid of my colleagues, I am offering them is meant too for all the shy and hesitant young girls who admire a good model's style and who want to acquire her confidence. They will already have learned that the swagger, the bravura and sometimes even that cheeky, winning grin most often start as an act, a trick that is learned at model school, or from this book. But soon the trick becomes natural, the act becomes fact.

The basic rules of communication—and that smile of confidence—are as applicable to everyday situations as to a morning in the studio. People take to someone who looks cheerful much more readily than a scowler—even though that scowl may be another mask, hiding the shyness behind it. Never let nervousness be translated into brusque off-handedness. Neither can you afford to look bored. It's a mistake to think that you'll attract helpful attention by obviously sulking and looking the odd girl out. You're more likely to offend than inspire positive reactions. Besides, bad manners only prolong the agony by delaying the positive contact which eventually makes friends and influences people.

Social situations have a competitive element all of their own. Often, the going can be tougher than a work situation—even than a photo session. At least when you're working, people are usually keen to help and give you encouragement.

After all, they've a vested interest in your getting it all right. But socially, it's sink or swim. Folk aren't so helpful—they're too busy helping themselves and only too ready to boost their own confidence by playing on your lack of it. So don't show it!

Knowing the rules helps; except that rules are made to be broken, and often are. Etiquette is a fragile code, subject to fashion. It may, in fact, be the 'in' thing to do the direct opposite to the procedure set out in the 'rule books'. You can't even trust the old table lore of starting with the cutlery on the outside of the place setting and working inwards, now that it's fashionable to eat everything with a fork. Your most trustworthy standby is the adage: 'When in Rome . . .' Watch everyone else, then copy them. Never bluff, though. You're far too likely to bluff or ad lib in the wrong direction.

There is a lot you can do to prepare yourself. As with modelling, you'll instantly feel more confident if you know you look good. If you're going to an important occasion, don't bite off more than you can chew. Never wear a complicated outfit that will take all your time and concentration to live up to. Perilously high heels, say, which are an effort to balance in; a very short skirt or a low neckline which will make you feel even more self-conscious and restrict your movements; material which creases easily so that you're scared to sit down—these will all play on your mind, cloud your cheerful expression and cramp your style.

Check too, that the outfit you plan is appropriate to the occasion. Dress etiquette is more flexible than any of the other social rules, as it obviously is much more dependent on fashion. Try to find out what other people are wearing before you go; then make sure your outfit is clean and well-pressed.

Don't experiment with your hair and make-up just before you're about to go out. Practise and work on your look— and have a semi-dress rehearsal the night before, so you get it all right on the night. Allow yourself enough time to get ready and to get there, so that you're completely relaxed when you arrive.

Walking into a room by yourself can be a nightmare, especially if you don't know a soul the other side of the door

'The essence of good taste is knowing just how far you can go'

or even what to expect. Prepare your defence—but be positive. Practise smiling every time you come into a room—any
room—until it becomes second nature. Not only will you
give pleasure to the people you know: you'll look pleasant
and at ease to the people you don't. You'll also look ap-
proachable, probably the last impression you want to give,
but nevertheless, here goes. . . .

First meetings can be awkward. The initial handshake in
itself can be the breaking point of your confidence, especially
if you see a hand looming towards you and both of yours are

occupied. It's a woman's privilege, not a man's, to offer a hand first. She doesn't have to but most do as it seems churlish not to. As a hostess, always shake hands with your guests. That says 'Thank you for coming, I'm glad you're here', especially when accompanied by the famous smile aimed right between the eyes! But as an employee or interview candidate you *never* extend your hand first. That implies you're putting *them* at ease which you are not in a position to do.

That over with, there is the gentle art of **conversation** to contend with. This can be horrific if it degenerates into a monologue of pure bluff in a desperate attempt to impress. Conversation is a danger zone of pitfalls and contradictions. If you don't know what you're talking about, you're bound to be caught out sooner or later. So you might just as well either deftly change the subject (using the 'problem' topic as a gentle link to lead into more familiar territory) or own up that although the subject sounds fascinating, you really know very little about it and would they mind telling you more. You're quite likely to be respected for your refreshingly candid approach and interest. Unless, of course, you *are* at an interview and should have done your 'homework' before you went along!

If you do know what you're talking about, don't overdo it and risk becoming a social bore. Your knowledge won't be respected unless someone is *genuinely* interested (watch their eyes), especially if you imply you know more than they do. Most people hate listening and love to talk. If you sweetly ask them the questions, you have the advantage. You may even learn something into the bargain.

If you strike an instant rapport with your new acquaintance, everything takes on a much rosier hue. But how do you get away from the 'crashing bore'? The short answer is, you don't, except *in extremis*. I am not here entering the whole perilous field of etiquette, but manners, which really mean consideration for others, are as necessary for a young model as for anyone else. And besides: (*a*) it may be your fault that the man is such a perfect bore and (*b*) deeper down he may prove to be the most interesting person in the room and an absolute love. Change the subject and remember to smile.

Sitting down to dinner presents fresh problems. It's often the unusual foods that you dread may appear—and sometimes do if only because the hostess has tried extra hard—which upset the apple cart. How do you attack them? Again, watch everyone else, and don't ad lib. Don't drink your wine too quickly either, in an attempt to stall for time. You need to keep a clear head. So take your time in sipping, instead. You'll feel mortified if you get so drunk you make a fool of yourself.

If you're in a restaurant and don't understand a word of the menu, ask your host to recommend a dish. Guesswork is far too dodgy—you may well end up with some impossible combinations which will really show you up. Keep an eye on the price of the meals you order and stick to the safety of the medium range. Choose the cheapest meal on the menu only if that's what you really want; but choosing expensive food is unfair to your host and not terribly good manners. Try not to order more courses than your host, unless he or she really urges you to do so. It will be embarrassing for you if you're the only one left eating. When in doubt, choose the same.

And never forget to say thank you. Models should thank everyone at a job for their contribution; the clients for their time at auditions and go-sees. Socially, you should never leave without thanking the host or hostess and usually it's polite to follow up your verbal thanks with a note in the next couple of days. At the other side of the event, you should confirm acceptance of an invitation as soon as you can, to allow your host to make the arrangements and cater accurately. If you can't make it at the last minute, always let your host know—by telephone if time is too tight for the post.

Of course, when you know people better and become accepted into their circle of friends, things immediately become more relaxed. Social niceties are softened and formality maybe dropped. But the basic responsibility of behaving fairly and honestly towards them is always maintained.

But you have to be accepted first. You have to make that initial contact. The model school smile that at first came from your own conscious effort made it all possible. When it's no longer an act, when it reveals the truth about the way you feel, then both your confidence and your acceptance are confirmed.

5
Dress Sense

Your clothes reflect your character. They can either establish you as someone with creative **flair** and instinctive **good taste**, or someone hopelessly lost for ideas, dressing only to fulfil the rules of convention and comfort. Superficial though it may seem, clothes do say a lot about you—people sum you up without even having to speak to you.

The **psychology of clothes** goes deeper than just plain vanity. Types of clothing typecast you, slotting you neatly into a social group, a profession and a lifestyle. Just as you'd recognise a policeman by his uniform, the plain clothes branch of humanity have their pet characteristics. If you see a man in a bowler hat and pinstripe trousers you automatically guess he's a city businessman—a banker, maybe. Someone in leathers and chains with spiky puce hair couldn't be anything else but a punk. They are obvious examples and we know that they may be wrong—the bowler hat may be a con-man and the punk a designer, but at least we are clear about the impressions they want to create. Our basic need to conform, however, can express itself in more subtle fashions. It isn't merely what you wear, but how you wear it that counts.

Two newish types have recently been caricatured as summing up London women to a tee. The 'Sloane Ranger' is a society girl from the upper end of the social scale. Harper's magazine, who invented the whole witty thing, writes a shade caustically that, inevitably, the Sloane Ranger is a Lucie Clayton graduate. Peter York, whose book *Style Wars* expands the legend further, claims that she is usually to be found living and working in the Chelsea/Knightsbridge parish. She is instantly, he says, to be recognised by her Hermès scarf (knotted just under the chin), her sleeveless quilted over-jacket (very Princess Anne!) and her green Wellington boots, even in town. She usually 'works' in a friend's art gallery or bookshop and spends her evenings with 'Hooray Henrys' who invariably are 'something in the city'. The other social group of girls are Mayfair Mercs (short for mercenaries). You can spot them by their perennial suntan, blonde highlighted hair, a penchant for tucking figure-hugging trousers into high-heeled calf-length boots (probably gold-trimmed) and a lot of gold jewellery, especially rings. Whereas the Sloane Rangers had most likely already 'got', Mayfair Mercs were the 'go getters', who would patrol the wine bars of the West End, hunting for stray company executives.

To avoid following these stereotypes or falling in too far with the masses, to establish your own individuality and keep them all guessing, you have to exercise your own imagination. Fashion magazines are excellent references but don't follow fashions slavishly. Adapt them to suit you both physically and psychologically. The essence of good taste is knowing just how far you can go. *In order to judge for yourself, you need to know the basic rules of dress sense—so that you can break them with flair.*

Dressing to fit

A model figure like the one described in Chapter 2 can wear any style and get away with it. That's why its owner is a model. But most girls don't have such luck. Girls in Britain are growing. A size 12 used to be the large side of standard, but nowadays 14 plus is more the norm, with busts and hips blossoming past 36 and 38 inches (91 and 96 cm) respectively. Even that wouldn't be so bad, if a simple scaling up of styles were all that was needed. But we don't conform to a mould; our distribution of inches can vary quite considerably. One girl can be pin-thin on top, then fill out around the hips and thighs; another can have the reverse problem. Then your

Elaborate accessories may not help unusual shapes

wardrobe becomes a question of **balance**. You may be cater-
ing for two different sizes in one body, but you must make
everything appear streamlined, in perfect **proportion**. You are
dressing to camouflage—to make the most of your good
points and hiding the not-so-good.

In a nutshell, unfussy streamlined styles, using colour continuity to carry the eye downwards, are the most flattering
for fuller figures, as they have both a slimming and elongating
effect. Fussy, over-elaborate designs which carry the eye
across, emphasise width, and make you look shorter. Tight,
clinging clothes show everything up. So unless you've that
model figure it is best to forget about these. Analysing your
body from the top, knowing exactly what to avoid is your

best guideline as a start. If you are top-heavy with a large bust and arms, you need to avoid width and bulk. Frills, pockets on the bust, tucks, double-breasted styles with wide revere collars all emphasise your size. Halter tops are especially unflattering to large busts and big arms. Avoid also busy or large patterns which draw attention to the area—especially T-shirts with motifs and slogans emblazened across your 'boobs'.

Be careful with **accessories**; scarves that knot at the front and sit on the bust, brooches and necklaces that use the area as a ledge to perch upon. Baggy dresses with yokes actually create that ledge.

Broad shoulders may not sound like a problem to the girl whose narrow sloping shoulders are the bane of her body. But to the top-heavy girl anything which emphasises her width could make her look like a wrestler. The ideal width for shoulders is around 15 inches (38 cm) all the way across. Anything past that should be treated with caution. Steer clear of padded or cap sleeves which obviously add to both height and width. Puff sleeves really pile on the inches, as do leg of mutton sleeves.

Large hips and thighs need special streamlining treatment. Skirts and trousers which are either too full or too tight will both emphasise the problem. Beware of dropped waistlines and hipster garments, belts that fall on the hips—they form the perfect outline for child-bearing hips and a bulging out at the top of the thighs. Pleated skirts cause problems. Box pleats especially draw attention to big thighs; even finer pleats, if they don't hang perfectly, accentuate the bulge beneath. Side pleats, kick pleats, slits at the front, back or sides also emphasise big thighs; layers which go crosswise add bulk if you catch them at the wrong levels. Far better to opt for an A-line skirt which skims the hips and doesn't go in again.

Drainpipe trousers stick too faithfully to your own outline, baggy trousers and jodhpurs will make you look even broader, and unless you have perfect legs the less said about shorts. . . . Your best options are the trouser styles with legs the same width all the way down; these balance you better.

Down to ground level, it's surprising how many people think **shoes** have little to contribute, apart from colour. How wrong this is. Styles have a significant effect on how long your legs look, how broad, slim, long or short your feet can seem. Shoes which are low-cut at the side broaden, as they leave a wide expanse on show. Bars across the instep have the same effect, whereas a T-bar lengthens, because it makes the eye travel downwards. Ankle straps emphasise chunky ankles (conversely they also show up slim ones). They're best avoided too if you've dumpy legs, as they break the continuation line of your shins down to your instep, which otherwise could have lengthened your look. Heels also count. The higher the heel, the slimmer your leg will look because firstly, you're forcing your calf muscle to contract in order to balance, and secondly, you're creating the illusion of extra length with your raised instep. Flat shoes cancel all this out. At the very tip of your feet, peep and open toes make your feet look longer, as more foot is exposed, although the more toes you actually see, the broader your foot will look.

Check your textures

It's vitally important to choose the correct materials to flatter your figure. The bad news first. The very worst textures for adding bulk and clinging to your figure are the knits—especially chunky-knits like bouclé, etc. T-shirt materials (like clingy cotton or cotton and nylon mixes) also show up every lump and bump and have an annoying tendency to lose their shape after a couple of washes. Because they have no weight to speak of, they also ride up easily! The fairly scrunchy texture of taffeta tends to cling. But the best figure-skimming fabrics which hang well are the slinkier silks or silk polyesters and medium-weight weaves like very fine wools, terylenes, heavy crêpes and gabardines.

What lengths can you go to?

Your **height** has a very great influence over your choice of styles, often creating as many problems as your weight.

Short girls (below 5′ 2″ or 157 cm) seem to have the toughest time as they can opt for neither very short, nor very long skirts. Mini or ra-ra length emphasises their short legs (especially if they're on the chubby side) and mid-calf or ankle length drowns them, making them look squatter.

Jackets have to be carefully chosen, too. Long, thigh-length jackets tend to look like shorter styles a couple of sizes too big. Best to stick to styles just past the waist, or a bona fide coat length, to just below the knee.

Small girls have to watch separates of any kind, really, as they tend to cut you in half. Choose simple lines in toning shades, so that there is still an element of continuity, to make you appear streamlined.

Everyone should be wary of **boot lengths**. The fashion for shorter boots gives rise to several problems if you're not endowed with virtually straight legs. Styles which cut mid-calf are the worst. They emphasise the calf muscle, making even the best-turned legs look strange. Shorter boots can make short legs look as if they're wearing 'wellies' and wider legs dumpier and chunkier still. (Calf-hugging longer boots which zip up the inside don't suit heavy calf muscles. Best go for the styles which are an equal width from the ankle upwards.)

Colour code

Choosing a colour to suit you involves several elements. As with style, your height and weight have to be considered as well as your natural colouring. Taking colours on their own, the basic rule is to remember that dark colours slim and throw features into relief, whilst bright colours draw attention and add bulk. Black and white (although technically 'non-colours' which do not appear in the natural spectrum) are extreme examples which prove the rule.

Colours in **patterns** cause more problems. The archetype of the pattern code is the stripe. We've already touched on the fact that horizontals add width because they lead the eye across and verticals add length and height. The width of the

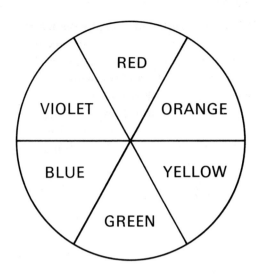

Colour wheel

stripes themselves and the brightness of the colours intensify or minimise the effect. (A positive panel of red contrasting with white has a greater effect than a narrow, subtle pinstripe, for example.)

Large, bright patterns of any kind have the same effect as horizontal stripes; in fact, patterns in general are not as universally flattering as single shades, well accessorised. So beware of even the most delicate of Liberty prints. Exquisite though it may be, it could easily look too 'busy'.

Chosing colours to suit your complexion isn't so difficult. Generally the ones you like are the ones which look good on you. It's an instinctive thing which you often carry through to the shades you chose for your home. Something about them sets you at your ease.

There are some rules, though, regarding hair colour and complexion. But they are by no means rigid. Make-up can have such an influence if used, as it should be, to correct your skin tone and act as an accessory to your clothes, that you can make virtually any colour work for you, if you use it carefully. Nevertheless, just bear the following in mind. Play up your **natural colouring** wherever possible. Colours to avoid are those which lie opposite to your skin tone on the colour spectrum. (Try to imagine a circular rainbow, with the rays fanning out, in order from the centre; red, orange and yellow follow round to green, blue and violet, so that violet actually comes all the way round to fall next to red at the start.) Florid, purplish complexions then should avoid limes and green-blues; sallow complexions steer clear of mauves; pale blue-white complexions avoid yellows. Pink-red complexions though actually do look better against toning shades, as anything else tends to emphasise the height of colour.

Eye-catching, bright colours can be doubly effective if you wear them near your face, and pick them up in your make-up shades. This brings all the attention upwards, highlighting your pretty smile and acting as a decoy from areas below which you may not be so happy about.

Blending and toning your tints are an art that some people seem to possess and carry out casually, whereas others have no clue. Continuity is your byword. As long as you chose a colour theme and stick to it, you'll be fine.

Try to analyse your shade and find out the colours which make it. (Your rainbow colour wheel should give you some idea.) Take green, for example. As it is a combination of blue and yellow, you can cheerfully and effectively use both blue, yellow and green together, perfectly naturally. (Don't believe folk who say blue and green are unlucky. They're a stunning combination.) But the minute you add a fourth alien to the natural order, like red, say, things begin to look cluttered.

The more shades which actually combine to make a new one, the more complex your blending will be. It's up to you to know when to stop. Brown is a good example. As it is a combination of red, blue and yellow, you can cheerfully accessorise it with those very shades and any of their by-products. Most effective, though, is to work around two or three shades of brown, say chocolate, tan and ochre, or for a lighter look, use beige as your base. When you are making a marked contrast with your colours, best stick to two only— black and red, for example, or navy and pink. But when you contrast with shades from either extreme of a single colour, you often find a third related shade adds brightness and relief.

Black-and-white, say, looks good with red accessories; navy and pale blue can be relieved with a strong pink or vibrant green.

You can make any colours work together, as long as you accessorise them purposefully and carry your theme through. Technically, none of nature's colours clash—it's only when humans try to fling them all together that they can look a mess.

Choosing your accessories

The key to accessorising well is to balance your points of interest—and know when to stop. Some girls have a compulsion to dress themselves up like Christmas trees as if they'd never get a chance to wear any of their things again. Be selective.

You should not, for example, wear a bangle with a frilled cuff—there's enough going on there anyway. Wear a ring instead. Similarly, fussy necklines don't need necklaces. High frilled collars will collide head on with dangling earrings, and have no need for scarves either. Very clean-cut designs with a distinct line to them can also look messy if you try to dress them up. Boat or square necks, say, are strong enough on their own—dangling necklaces get in the way. Far better to take the interest upwards with a really nice pair of earrings and let the design have it.

Moving lower down, belts can do a lot to emphasise a neat waistline and co-ordinate separates. (They can also emphasise bulky or messy waists and hips, as we've already seen.) But unless you want all the attention to hover around your middle, you need something at either end. A matching pair of shoes, say, and a toning scarf or earrings. Beware of bangles and belts. As they fall more or less in the same area, they can fight each other.

Keep both the colour and the medium of your accessories consistent both with themselves and with your outfit. You can use them to add colour contrasts, but never contrast them with themselves. Brassy bangles, for example, don't go with fine gold chains and diamanté necklaces. Silver earrings clash

'A compulsion to dress like a Christmas tree' (see page 43)

head on with gold jewellery on the rest of your body. Plastic is best kept for a lively daytime look—it can look cheap for evening wear.

Lastly, wherever you wear an accessory, don't just view it in isolation. Look at how it affects your whole outfit, from top to bottom. It's only then that you will gain a true sense of balance and perception.

Building a wardrobe

You've established which styles and colours suit you, now how do you put them all together?

The perfect working wardrobe should consist of a selection of clothes which you can either wear on their own, or to interact with each other—the **mix and match** system. Separates are versatile friends, if you can wear them. A basic starting point of a pair of trousers, a skirt, a sweater and a blouse already gives you four complete outfits, if you 'cross-reference' them. Accessories ring the changes and make garments look different outfits entirely, so a good stock of scarves, belts, shoes and jewellery is something you can gradually build up as you go. Shoes, though, cost a fortune. So at first concentrate on the basics: black court shoes and evening shoes, plus a pair of sporty flat shoes for trousers and black or brown boots. Strappy sandals, etc., can come later.

Try to avoid sticking to the same old shades all the time, though. Add a splash of fresh colour from time to time, either with a completely new get-up when you can afford it, or some bright, matching accessories. Even girls who dress to camouflage don't have to be slaves to their shortcomings. Someone who always wears black, for example, as opposed to a variety of dark shades punctuated by brighter trimmings will eventually make people think she's got something to hide, instead of throwing them off the scent.

Make sure your undercover story is in tune with the top show. Model agencies suggest their models should always have both flesh-coloured and black underwear (pants, waistslips and bras) plus a strapless flesh-coloured bra which can be worn with shoulderless tops. A selection of coloured tights, including black and pale flesh colour which tone with your outfits makes all the difference.

A sense of occasion

Some things were meant for daywear, others for evening. You'd hike in one outfit, type in another, go to dinner in something completely different. One of the biggest blunders you can make is to find yourself out of step with the crowd and nothing is more guaranteed to sap your confidence.

As clothes become more casual and practical social rules grow hazy, the pedantry of office lore especially falls apart at the seams. Most firms, for example, let girls wear trousers, with the ironic exception of the Chanel company, who seem to have forgotten that Coco founded the trouser suit trend.

Jeans and jumpers seem practically universal, both in offices and outside them. If they're clean and you're comfy, why not? Do you perform any worse in them than in a skirt? Nevertheless, if your office tradition bans jeans—be sensible. There are other places in which you can be a pioneer. . . . If you're not sure what you should be wearing just keep your eyes open and follow the trend. Follow too, these general guidelines.

Styles largely speak for themselves, but fabrics can instantly put a garment in its place. Natural fibres like wool, cotton and leather are mostly daywear mediums which have a more casual feel than say velvet, crêpe de chine, taffeta, satin, and floaty, lacy and transparent fabrics, which are mostly worn for evening. Silk bridges the gap. You can wear a silk blouse (or a similar polyester look-alike) with trousers in the day with a skirt for dinner, or make up into a dress or dress-suit for special occasions.

The real traps are the clothes that follow neither one set of rules nor the other. Fine, delicately coloured chamois leather pantaloons, say, could easily be termed too dressy for daytime or too casual for a formal occasion. Few people bother too much with convention but you'd think twice before you'd wear them to a dinner dance.

Don't risk it. When in doubt, ask someone else what they'll be wearing; if you can't, do a subtle check with the host.

6
Diet and Exercise

Keeping in trim means keeping in work. A sensible approach to what you eat and how you move is not only the key to your health and good looks, it ensures you perform to your maximum ability, whatever you do. To a model, diet is doubly important. A weight fluctuation or out-of-condition skin and hair could mean loss of work. As I have explained in Chapter 2, the 'model size' is very clearly defined and doesn't allow for much deviation. A clothes peg is by nature a slender creature whose curves do not intrude on the lines of the all-important garment. You are employed to show off whatever the client hangs on you—so you must be constantly slender, graceful, supple and vital. And that means a level-headed, dedicated approach to diet and exercise.

The fuel for beauty

The first stage of your healthy eating programme is to understand your **nutrients** and what exactly they will do for you. Think of your body as a beautiful machine. It constantly needs fuel to supply it with energy, maintain all its parts and repair it when some components break down. Different foods have different nutritional values and in varying quantities. Up to now, no one has managed to invent a 'complete food', supplying all the body needs—hence the need for a balanced diet to supply the full nourishing range.

Our bodies, however, don't need exactly the same amounts of each food group. Some nutrients can be stored in the body and others cannot and need to be taken daily. The plot thickens when you learn that certain nutrients, especially vitamins, interact and aid each other's function in the body. A deficiency of one could hold up the work of the others.

A thorough examination of each of the components of nutrition is contained in Appendix 1 at the end of this book, for the time when you need to know more. Meanwhile, for a more 'instant' impression of their work, let's put them into practice by studying the foods which contain them.

What is a balanced diet?

Broadly speaking, to meet your vitamin and mineral quotas, your diet must (*a*) be as varied as possible and (*b*) comply with fairly set nutritional guidelines. The old 'meat and two veg.' lore isn't too misleading, especially if your main meal of the day is based on a moderate portion of lean meat or fish (vegetarians can substitute cheese or pulses) plus one green, leafy vegetable and another root. Your daily pattern is complete is you start with a wholemeal toast or cereal breakfast (with a thin scraping of butter or margarine, or just enough milk to make the cereal palatable) and keep your secondary meal light—low fat cheese, say, with salad and a piece of fruit.

More specifically, foods fall into five basic groups from which you must compile your daily eating programme. Obviously, you don't need equal portions of each foodstuff, nor do you need to plough your way through all the members of all the groups in one day! Variety isn't just the spice of life— it's the life source. So try a different set of combinations every day of the week.

Note that the 'daily needs' are the equivalent, in food terms, of the minimum daily requirement. You don't necessarily need to eat the full amounts of any one food suggested. You should, however, learn to cross-reference the sections to gain a picture of your daily balance of foods.

Group 1. Dairy products

Milk, cheese, cream, yoghurt, etc.

Provides: protein, fat, calcium, vitamins A, B₂ and D.
Daily needs: ½ pint (300 ml) of milk; *or* 2 oz. (60 g) cheese.

Group 2. Meat, fish and eggs

Including poultry, offal and shellfish.

Provides: protein, fat, vitamins B₁, B₂, nicotinic acid, iron.
Daily needs: 3 oz. (90 g) meat *or* 2 eggs or 4 oz. (120 g) fish.

Group 3. Fruit and vegetables

Provides: iron, vitamins A, B₁, C.
Daily needs: 1 orange *or* 4 oz. (120 g) cooked vegetables.

Group 4. Fats

Including butter, margarine, vegetable oils.

Provides: fat, vitamins A and D.
Daily needs: 1 oz. (30 g) butter *or* margarine.

Group 5. Cereals and pulses

Including bread, flour, pasta, rice, nuts, beans.

Provides: protein, carbohydrate, calcium, iron, vitamins B₁, B₂, nicotinic acid.
Daily needs: 4 slices bread *or* 4 oz. (120 g) nuts *or* 8 oz. (230 g) cooked pasta.

Watching your weight

To maintain a perfect **figure balance**, the amount of energy you consume must equal the amount of energy you burn. This includes both tangible activity (several movements and exercise) and your **basic metabolic rate**—the rate at which your body carries out its vital functions (the involuntary actions of heartbeat, breathing, digestion, growth, repair, etc., which are vital to life and which take up two thirds of our energy intake). Your weight may fluctuate a couple of pounds from day to day. Your period, for example, could account for a pound or so of fluid weight, which is lost steadily after Day One. You may have eaten a particularly lavish meal one day, which you'll naturally balance out with leaner fare the next. But taken on a week to week basis, if everything is working well (including you!) your weight should stay pretty stable.

Sudden losses in weight can be due to a change in lifestyle and meal patterns (you've just begun a new job, say), when the adrenalin is pumping through your veins, you're naturally a touch nervous and most probably more active than normal. You may even feel a little 'high' as your system is revved up and your thinking processes swing into full gear. You'll probably find your weight loss bottoms out at around half a stone, when your body has had a chance to adjust to its new patterns. But drastic weight losses call for a medical check, just to make double-sure that nothing's amiss.

But it's weight gain that is the problem for fashion-conscious young ladies. And for the model, it's a disaster. As I said at the very beginning of this book, the camera isn't totally on your side—it has the effect of making you look around five pounds plumper than you actually are, so models have to be that bit skinnier than the average 'clothes peg'. Thankfully, the dangerous days of the Sixties, when girls starved themselves silly to look like Twiggy, are long over. The look of the Eighties is healthy, strong and firm, with curves neatly moulded in all the right places; the look, in fact, that bears testimony to an enlightened age of healthy eating and exercise.

Nevertheless, neither the model business nor the rag trade on which it is so dependent has much time for spare inches. And the measurements printed on your model cared are the ones you *have* to stick by, or the client will want to know the reason why.

How to lose weight sanely and safely

Excess weight is a store of unused energy which the body converts to fat after it has burned up all it requires for our daily activities. To lose weight, we must either cut down the amount of fresh energy we take in, or increase our levels of activity to force the body to draw on its reserves. Exercise is therefore the no-diet method of weight loss—we'll deal with that later on in the chapter. Cutting down our energy intake—or dieting—can be done by two basic methods.

The calorie-controlled diet

Calories are themselves energy units, and all foods contain calories to a greater or lesser degree. The higher the fat content of a food, the higher the energy and calorie value which unfortunately accounts for a feeling of weakness and irritability on some severely calorie-restricted diets.

A normal everyday diet should take up 2,000 to 2,200 calories daily, to fulfil the needs of a healthy average working girl. Most calorie-controlled diets, however, hover around the 1,200 mark—a considerable drop (anything less than that should be followed on a short-term basis of no more than five days, preferably when you're not working too hard). You can easily make up your own calorie-controlled diet by investing in one of the many booklets of calorie values, setting yourself a daily limit and counting the calories of each meal. This gives you *carte blanche* to eat a wide range of foods— but it does lead you into the temptation of eating only the foods you like, rather than the foods you need for balanced nutrition. You could lose weight on chocolate bars, so long as you stuck to around 1,200 calories worth daily. But they would be pretty expensive in both calorie and health terms. Your aim should be to build your diet from each of the food groups mentioned previously. Your protein intake should account for around 50 per cent of your daily calories, with the rest taken up by fresh vegetables (thankfully sparing on calories), fruit with carbohydrates kept to the minimum, but nevertheless present.

Calorie control inevitably relies on accurate portion control—fine if you stick to pre-packed foods with the weights neatly listed on the labels. But real accuracy often entails weighing food, and that can prove tedious, time-consuming and inconvenient especially if you're working and can't always prepare a packed lunch. Until experience has made you expert enough to judge portions at a glance, it's best to stick to 'single unit' foods like pieces of fruit, vegetables, spoonfuls of cottage cheese, slices of bread or bread rolls which you can check against your ever-ready calorie list. That way you can still function as a social animal.

Low carbohydrate diet

Restricting your **carbohydrate** intake is also a method of cutting down on calories. Starchy and sugary foods are limited or cut out altogether in favour of protein-rich foods such as meat, fish and cheese. The argument for low-carbohydrate diets is that although fats are completely unrestricted, having no carbohydrate values whatsoever, the fat intake should be automatically cut by eating lean meat and fish, and the other foods which involve fat (pastries, sauces, chips and bread which is usually spread with butter or margarine) are heavily restricted if not eliminated completely. The major pitfall of this diet, though, is to eat larger than normal quantities of carbohydrate-free proteins, so the fat and calorie values creep up and tip the balance. Fruit and some vegetables are also restricted, which might not suit everyone's palate. And alcohol is prohibited!

But for all that, low-carbohydrate diets are easy to calculate and follow, as no weighing of food is involved. Each foodstuff represents certain units, or 'points' (one unit equals five grams of carbohydrate), and you're generally allowed around ten points daily. Nutritionally, low-carbohydrate diets make sound sense, and they are high in energy which means working girls won't flag on the job. For this reason Premier, one of the top model agencies, recommend the famous Scarsdale diet to their models because they know that it's composed of varied and balanced meals and is safe enough to follow over a two-week period, with an average weight loss of around seven pounds. (The sensational ten pounds usually associated with two weeks on the Scarsdale is usually only achieved by women who are significantly over-weight. Models should be shifting pounds—not stones!) As well as obtaining a copy of the Scarsdale diet from your local bookshop, you can also buy booklets listing carbohydrate values, to make up your own Ten Point Plan.

General points to remember when dieting

(1) Never diet over a long period of time without checking your health with your doctor first.

(2) I can't overstress the importance of a **nutritionally balanced** diet. The basis of both calorie and carbohydrate controlled diets should be the daily 'musts': $\frac{1}{2}$ oz. butter or margarine (or 1 oz. low-fat spread), $\frac{1}{4}$ pint milk, 1 thin slice of wholemeal bread.

(3) If you can't wean yourself off sweet tea and coffee, substitute sweeteners for sugar and drink only low-calorie softdrinks. When in doubt, stick to mineral or soda water.

(4) You will probably find that your weight loss is quite dramatic in the first week—three to seven pounds in some cases. This is due to the body's immediate reaction of drawing on the glycogen stores in the liver and muscles, plus a couple of pounds worth of fluid loss. Fat itself is much harder to shift and this accounts for the more steady realistic loss of around two pounds in Week 2, so don't be downhearted. If you are very overweight and need to carry on for several weeks (with your doctors permission) you may find you eventually reach a plateau, or 'stick', when your body adapts to its more stringent regime. A week of maintenance dieting (up your intake by around 200 calories or 2 carbohydrate units) or, conversely, a restriction of the same amount will usually jolt it into action again.

(5) Although they should be unnecessary if your diet is nutritionally balanced, a course of multivitamins plus minerals is a wise investment to ensure your body is getting all it needs.

(6) Do not weigh yourself every single day. Once a week, at the same time of day, wearing the same clothes gives a more accurate reading of your true weight loss.

(7) Don't expect dieting to treat one area of the body only (or 'spot reduce'). Your face is the first to register loss (models beware the gaunt, hungry-eyed look which fights make-up), with your bust and waist following a close second. A cruel quirk of fate makes your hips and thighs the hardest to slim down, as they are prime target areas for regular fat stores.

(8) Know when to **stop dieting**. The slimmers' disease anorexia nervosa is a killer long-term. But you'll lose work, perspective and friends long before that. A physical and psychological inability to increase your food intake to a healthy level after dieting is a danger signal, as much as the more classic symptoms of 'bingeing' and 'purging'. It's a chilling thought that anorectics are rarely successfully cured.

The Lucie Clayton diet

This diet is ideal for working girls, as it's flexible enough to fall in with most lunch and dinner arrangements, whether in a canteen, restaurant or a working studio 'picnic'. At around 1,200 calories daily, it isn't drastic, so you shouldn't feel worn out after three days' solid dedication. But it will ensure a steady weight loss of two to three pounds weekly. Think of it as 'being careful' more than following a rigid routine. You can swap dinner for lunch, for example, but never skip meals.

The diet has been worked out to give you all the daily nutrition you need for your health and looks. Taking liberties with your daily allowances (stretching your butter quota for example) isn't on either. It's surprising how the calories creep up with an 'accidental' slip of the hand. It's your loss, remember!

Daily allowances: ½ oz. butter or margarine (1 oz. low-fat spread); ¼ pint of milk (½ pint skimmed milk). Dress salads with lemon juice, vinegar, and season with herbs and pepper, but *no* oil and steady on the salt. Black coffee and

tea are unlimited (or take them with milk from your allowance). Bovril and herb teas are also free and make comforting
perks between meals, as does mineral water with a slice of
lemon. Use artificial sweeteners if you must (no sugar). Weigh
everything you can at first so that you get used to judging
your portions by eye, when scales are not available.

Breakfast: 1 medium glass of unsweetened grapefruit or orange
juice (or mix half and half).
1 egg, poached, boiled, scrambled (butter and milk from
allowance).
1 slice of wholemeal bread (butter from allowance).

Lunch: 2 oz. lean meat, poultry, fish or cheese.
1 average portion (around 2 tablespoons) green vegetables or salad.
1 slice of wholemeal bread (butter from allowance).
1 portion of fresh fruit (not banana).

Dinner: 2 oz. lean meat, poultry or fish.
1 portion of green vegetables.
1 portion of salad, mixed.
1 oz. cheese.
1 water biscuit or starch-reduced crispbread (butter
from allowance).

The logic of exercise

We need to exercise for three basic reasons. First, the body is
a machine which needs to be used regularly to remain efficient. Joints need to be toned, muscles need to be kept active
and strong and our heart and lungs must be trained to perform to tip-top capacity. Secondly, we need to burn up fuel
which we take in the form of food. A surfeit of energy which
is not burned up, as we have already seen, is stored in the
body as fat, which is (*a*) an unhealthy strain on the heart and
(*b*) downright ugly. Lastly, we can exercise to firm and trim
slack muscles and areas of flab which get in the way of an
otherwise perfect figure.

Exercise is extremely rewarding, as it actually does become

easier with practice and you can feel your body becoming fitter. Suddenly, you're generating your own energy as your body responds more readily to the work-outs you put it through. You feel livelier because your components are being allowed to do their job properly and you feel healthier and more relaxed mentally. We were never designed to sit around. So it's hardly surprising that office jobs, ever-available transport and a society intent on generally taking the passive, easier way out are generating nothing more than sluggish, poorly functioning systems and 'rusty' bodies. What *is* surprising, though, is that you only need around ten minutes of exercise daily to pep yourself up and keep in trim.

The heart of the matter

The key to fitness is in your very heartbeat itself. Your muscles need oxygen in order to work, and your heart pumps

Star jump

it to them via the bloodstream. Normally, a steady pulse is sufficient to supply enough oxygen for normal muscular activity. But when any greater effort is involved (as in running, say), your breathing becomes faster and deeper to supply the heart with more oxygen. Your heart in turn beats faster, to pump the increased oxygen supply to the muscles, which urgently need it. Far from being dangerous to push your body to these limits, your heart actually benefits from the practice, and gradually strengthens and adapts to its more demanding role, the more work it gets to do. (Doctors say you should run out of breath at least three times a day.)

What the heart doesn't take too kindly to is sudden bursts of extreme activity when it isn't used to it. For this reason, you should gradually build up your levels of exercise, slowly increasing your stamina, so that your heart can actually keep pace with your enthusiasm. Never *force* yourself to the point of pain. If it hurts, stop and rest immediately.

Building stamina

Aerobics is a much abused word but for most it means giving your heart and lungs a thorough work-out, boosting the oxygen levels in the bloodstream. In fact, you could easily fit them into your life style. If every day you jogged or walked briskly part-way to work, then used the stairs instead of lifts wherever possible, you would be making a significant contribution to your aerobic programme.

Cycling is good exercise (and economical) and **swimming** is one of the finest there is, as you can exercise every part of the body in the process. **Dancing** has the advantage that not only does it build up stamina, but it encourages suppleness, grace and the heightened sense of body awareness vital to a relaxed, confident model, especially when she's doing shows. Model agencies often urge their girls to join dance classes like ballet or modern jazz.

Some models prefer to train in a local gym, especially with or without weights, to keep fit and trim. You can also 'work out' at home. An early warm-up session wakes your system and tunes your body ready for the day's work ahead. Try this:

Jog on the spot for a count of 50. Without stopping, do 10 star jumps (arms and legs together, then apart) and then straight 50 more 'jogs'. Rest for 30 seconds. Do 5 squat jumps (crouch, back straight, buttocks sitting on heels, fingertips touching the floor for balance, then spring up straight and down again). Rest for 30 seconds. Then follow with 10 press-ups (breathe in as you raise your chest, out as you lower it, keep your back straight), another 30-second rest, then 10 bench steps with each leg leading (step onto a low box and off again as if you were running up and down a single stair).

If this routine is a *tremendous* strain (and you are really gasping for breath), halve the movements and the rest periods and gradually work up to the full amount by increasing daily. Otherwise, try to build up slowly to double the movements with half the time in between, until you can perform the whole sequence twice without stopping.

Trimming and toning your figure

You can literally lose inches without even thinking of a diet, by regular exercises to tone the muscles, break down excess fat deposits and firm your skin. Your work is now your investment for the future. Call it self-preservation! The following exercises are designed to treat the body from head to toe:

To prevent a double chin: Open your mouth as wide as you can and let your head drop back. Now try to close your mouth. Straighten your head up again and repeat five times.

To firm the bust and upper arms: Clasp hands, palms inwards at chest level, keeping your elbows horizontal and at shoulder level. Push your palms together ten times, as if you're trying to squash something between them. You should feel the pectoral muscles jump. Rest, then repeat. Build up to six sets of ten.

To tone the sides of the waist: Stand with your feet together

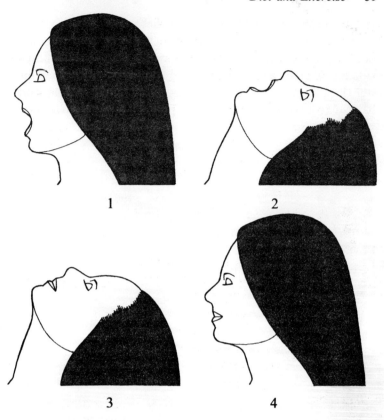

To prevent a double chin

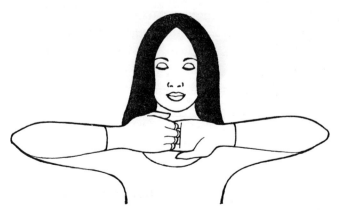

To firm the bust and upper arms

and then separate them by a few inches to about the width of your hips. Raise your left arm above your head, angling over towards the left, keeping the right arm straight at your side for balance. Reach now to the right as far as you can (you should feel the pull on your waist muscles) and stretch eight times. Repeat to the other side. Build up to six repeats each side.

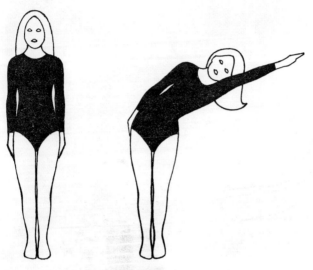

To tone the sides of the waist

To trim your stomach: Lie on the floor, hands under your lower back. Draw your knees into your chest, keeping your ankles together. Slowly straighten out your legs again until they are around 2 inches (5 cm) above the floor. Slowly draw them in again. Repeat five times, building to ten without touching the floor.

For trim thighs: On your back, legs straight, arms at sides as before, raise your right leg right up to 90° taking care to keep it straight. Slowly lower and repeat with the left leg. Repeat fifteen times, building up to thirty.

For supple and trim ankles: Sit on the floor, back and legs straight. Raise your right leg 2 inches (5 cm) off the ground and flex your foot as far back and as hard as you can. Then arch your instep, forcing your toes down to point to the ground. Repeat with your left leg. Raise your right leg again,

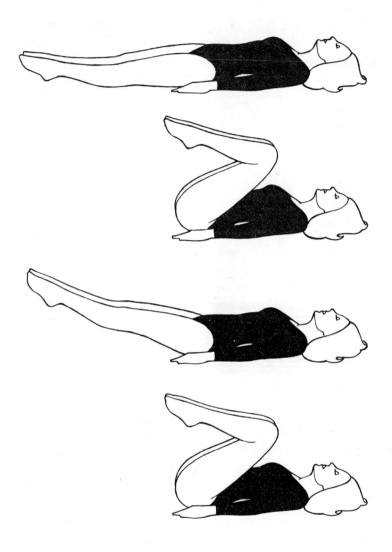

Stomach trimming—but remember hands should support the lower back

then circle your foot six times clockwise, then reverse. Repeat with your left leg. Repeat the whole sequence five times, building to ten. This exercise also strengthens and trims the calf and thigh muscles (see illustrations on page 62).

1

2

3

4

Exercise for trim ankles (see page 60)

7
Hygiene—Good Clean Sense

The motto for hygiene, of course, is 'keep it clean'. But there's more to it than simply soap, water and deodorants. Your ideal is a question of balance—how to maintain your social commitment to sweet-smelling cleanliness whilst also maintaining your respect for your body, or more immediately in this context, your skin.

Your skin is the largest and surely one of the hardest working organs of your body. Unfortunately, it is the result of this essential industriousness that causes so much embarrassment and discomfort. Your skin controls body temperature and eliminates waste by perspiration, which eventually smells. Modern society turns its nose up at natural odours, so we frantically try to staunch both sweat and smell by using anti-perspirants.

To function properly, skin must hold an adequate moisture quota. It produces natural oil, or **sebum**, from its pores both to seal in the moisture and to form an antiseptic barrier of acids and alcohol on the surface and so stave off bacterial invasion. A shiny face might be thanks to a perfectly functioning skin, but cosmetically it causes problems. We fight back with oil-stripping agents which temporarily solve our superficial problem, but may work directly against our skin's well-being. Good clean sense, then, is a matter of moderation. Understand your skin and its functions—then do the best for both of you.

The structure of the skin

Skin is composed of two basic layers, both containing several more layers in their own right. The deepest layer, or **dermis**, houses sweat glands, capillaries, nerves and hair follicles and is composed of elastic bundles of **collagen**, the tissue which supports the skin and gives it plump suppleness. It is divided from the top layer, or **epidermis**, by a thin but tough membrane, which keeps moisture in and harmful substances out of the dermis. Just above it is the basal layer of the epidermis. Cells at this level divide and grow, moving upwards as they do so, until they reach the very top layer. Then they become completely dead, horny flakes of **keratin**. Keratin acts like a suit of armour; oiled by sebum, it helps prevent dehydration and infection. As the sun is one of the most damaging, dehydrating and ageing enemies of the skin, a further defence mechanism is a sun tan. This is produced when the melanocytes, or pigment cells, in the basal layer release their **melanin** to form a natural sunscreen. The skin also contains a dormant substance which, when exposed to sunlight, is converted into vitamin D to feed our bones.

Two types of sweat glands are housed in the skin, each playing its part in keeping the body from overheating and ridding it of waste materials. Eat a spicy meal, and you could very well find that your skin, as well as your breath, smells faintly of garlic the next day.

The **apocrine glands** are the most 'trouble' to us. They are found under the arms, around the nipples and sex organs, and are sexual in nature, in that they come into play around puberty and are said to secrete chemicals which are attractive to the opposite sex, called **pheromones**.

The **eccrine glands** are spread over the rest of the skin area and secrete a thinner, more 'innocent' type of sweat, largely to control temperature. Or they can be triggered off by nervousness: hence clammy hands and forehead.

Unbelievable as it may seem, freshly secreted sweat doesn't smell much at all. But the bacteria ever-present on the skin's surface attack and decompose the perspiration, producing the characteristic smell—especially in warm nooks like the armpits and groin, where sweat can't evaporate quickly. These areas obviously need frequent special treatment.

To bath or not to bath?

A good long soak in a nice warm bath is almost everyone's idea of comfort and luxury. There's nothing quite like
it for relaxing muscles and calming your nerves after a long
tiring day. But baths don't necessarily do the skin any
favours. Highly alkaline bubble baths, salts and even soap
can go that bit too far with their efficiency, stripping off the
skin's natural oils and interfering with its protective acid
mantle. Soaking has a further drying effect. In self-defence,
the skin pumps out its own moisture to dilute the strong
chemicals in the bath water—thus depleting its own natural
reserves.

Showers are far safer. Not only is it impossible to soak in
a shower, thus cutting down the risk of dehydration, but
you've a far better chance of thoroughly rinsing the skin of
soap and shower gel. As a daily first thing in the morning

Shower attachment—more invigorating than a bath

splash, a shower is also much more invigorating—peps you up rather than calming you down.

Don't think that because your bathroom doesn't have a *bona fide* shower unit you're denied this optimum choice. You can easily buy rubber shower attachments which fit on-to your bath taps. You simply direct the spray as you stand or kneel in the bath.

Whether you choose a bath or shower, keep the water temperature moderately warm—not too hot—and be sparing with your bath products. Never use an antiseptic or dis-infectant in the water. Far from protecting your skin, it could kill off the body's natural and necessary bacteria, leaving the skin open to infection. Use plenty of body lotion afterwards to replace the lost oils and prevent further dehydration of the skin. (A few drops of baby oil in a bath can also help buffer off the stripping effects of detergents and soap.)

Make sure you're absolutely dry before you put your clothes on. Dampness in creases and crevices not only causes soreness, but can also provide a congenial habitat for irritat-ing fungal infections and cracked skin. Gently pat these areas dry then sprinkle on absorbent talcum powder—baby powder is fine-textured, bland and soothing.

Which deodorant?

A straightforward deodorant contains chemicals that attempt to prevent the odour of perspiration only. It will do nothing to inhibit the perspiration itself.

An **anti-perspirant** deodorant works in three ways. It con-tains chemicals, usually aluminium salts, which block the sweat ducts, inhibiting perspiration; a germicide which inter-feres with the action of bateria on the sweat itself; and a light fragrance which acts as a back-up device, masking any odour which does form. Frankly, anti-perspirants are very rarely 100 per cent effective. They simply help to cut down sweat and smell. There is a limit to the amount of chemicals which can be safely used on the skin without the risk of inflamma-tion. Besides, if a product could completely block the sweat ducts this could cause, in very hot weather, a rupture of the glands themselves and even more severe swelling.

So which products are the most effective? Most people find that roll-ons or formulae which are directly applied to the skin are more successful than the aerosol sprays, although some people like the temporary absorbency of the dry-powder formulae. There is also an environmental standpoint against the use of aerosols of any kind. Scientists believe that the chemicals used in the propellants may be steadily polluting the atmosphere.

How do you get the best performance from your anti-perspirant? *Do not apply it straight after your bath or shower*, but let your body cool down and your pores become receptive. Keep the product confined to your underarms only. Remember, you need to sweat and your aim is to reduce wetness and odour only where it is the most obvious and embarrassing. All products work the best on clean, smooth skin. Underarm hair can act as a barrier between your product and your skin. (See Chapter 8 for the safe removal of body hair.) But take care your anti-perspirant doesn't irritate your freshly 'de-fuzzed' skin. Wait until the product is completely dry before you dress, so that the maximum is on your skin and the minimum on your clothes. If (like most of us) you loathe the obtrusive and sometimes sickly smells of the perfumed anti-perspirants, and you can't find an unperfumed product you like, look for the 'blue' or 'green' fragrances. They are usually so much more fresh and subtle than the 'pink' ones.

You can help your anti-perspirant also by wearing loose-fitting clothes in natural materials, so that the air can circulate around your body and the perspiration can evaporate. Tight-fitting nylon garments are your worst enemy. The closely woven texture of stretch fabrics, for example, cling to the skin, block off air and have poor absorbent qualities. Cotton underwear (or at the very least, nylon pants and bras lined with cotton) are both absorbent and non-irritant, as are cotton socks. In the winter, pure wool is both warmer and healthier as it allows your body to 'breathe' and won't trap stale air.

If you need to use a foot refresher spray or deodorant, spray it on clean, dry feet. (For hints on pedicure and hard skin removal, see Chapter 8.) Deodorised inner soles act as absorbent back-ups if you've a real 'sweaty feet' problem.

But make sure there's enough room in your shoes for both the inner soles and your feet. Cramped feet lead to corns.

Keeping your clothes clean

Clothes don't actually have to look grubby to retain perspiration and smell stale. A jumper or blouse, say, worn several days on the trot will show you up even though you've bathed every morning. The most practical clothes are the ones made of natural fibres like cotton, linen or wool, which allow air in and out and won't irritate or allow air to become trapped next to the skin—like nylon, for example. The looser your clothes, the more freely air can circulate, allowing perspiration to evaporate. (One up for the baggy tops and trousers fashion.)

Ideally, you should be meticulous about changing 'one day only' clothes, like underwear, hosiery and blouses. Give heavier outer-clothes like skirts and jumpers an airing at the end of the day by hanging them outside if it's fine, or at least outside the wardrobe overnight before you put them away. Try not to wear anything—especially shoes—two days running, to allow them to 'cool down'. Remember, fresh clothes go hand in hand with a careful washing and deodorising routine to keep *you* fresh.

Intimate hygiene: how far should you go?

Obviously, your starting point to the hygiene of your more intimate zones begins with careful daily washing. But considering the essential dual role of the pubic area, there is the temptation to fall into the trap of a 'freshness fetish' which may not be entirely natural, nor, in fact, necessary.

Because of its special duties, the pubic area has powerful antibacterial agents of its own. The vagina, for example, secretes an acid, slightly sticky substance, which protects it from infection. This can become an uncomfortable source of embarrassment, especially after ovulation (fourteen days after the start of your last period) when the vagina steps up production and the secretion itself becomes more glutinous. So how do you overcome this? One thing's for certain—you can't control it, nor should you try. It is extremely dangerous to attempt internal washing or douching, as to rid the vagina of its natural protection means leaving it open to infection.

Feminine deodorants are also unnecessary and dangerous. First, they can cause irritation through interference with the natural acid balance of the area; but more sinister, they can mask the alarm signals and odours of an infection or more serious disorder. In its healthy state, the secretion is virtually colourless and odourless. But any change in colour or smell (menstruation apart, of course) spells trouble. Visit your doctor immediately. You may have an infection—and a responsibility both to yourself and others to get it treated quickly.

For the most part, though, the recent introduction of discreet 'mini-pads' (lightweight versions of the thicker sanitary towels) to the market provides the safest answer to dealing with the wetness problem. In fact, as a model (or anyone else who tries other people's clothes on) they offer you protection, as well as ensuring you keep yourself to yourself, so to speak.

Since the recent tampon scare in America, most hygienists are dubious about the habitual use of even the smallest of tampons when one is not actually menstruating. But from a working girl's point of view, they're still the most effective safeguard when a period is imminent and you need to 'be prepared'. They are also the most discreet and easily disposable form of sanitary wear, with the least risk of odour. Still, say the doctors, *take care*. Change tampons regularly, and switch to a smaller size or towel towards the end of your period when your loss is lighter. Never try to force a tampon into place. If at first you don't succeed, wait until your muscles relax or wear a towel instead. It's much safer and less painful. Furthermore, modern towels are contoured to echo the shape of your body and so are less bulky and more comfortable. Most simply adhere to your pants, so fiddling around with belts and safety pins are thankfully a thing of

the past. You can also flush most towels down the toilet—
but check on the packet first.

Should you use a feminine deodorant at this time? Really,
if you wash carefully, you simply shouldn't need one. Although you may like to use a hygienic tissue, like a baby
wipe, when changing during the day.

Sound teeth and fresh breath

A chapter on hygiene would be incomplete without some dis-
cussion on the care of the mouth. Bad breath is something
we dread even more than bad teeth. It's certainly more immediately apparent and doubly embarrassing and unpleasant
for a make-up artist, for instance, who has to spend hours
close to your face and right in the firing line.

Bad breath is caused by a number of things. Simply not
eating or drinking for a number of hours is one cause which
dieters will quickly acknowledge. A cup of herbal tea now
and again can freshen your mouth without upsetting your
calorie intake. But more sinister causes are poorly cleaned
teeth and gum disease which *won't* suddenly vanish with a
mouthwash.

The importance of cleaning your teeth thoroughly and
properly cannot be stressed enough. Bad breath aside, it's
your *smile* we're talking about. And whether you are a model
or an attractive girl in any profession, your smile is very much
your passport whilst you're young and an undeniable asset
when you're that bit older. A good set of teeth gives you the
confidence to project yourself through a natural, uninhibited
smile. So oral hygiene makes extra sense from a psychological
standpoint.

The mouth is one of the body's most fertile breeding
grounds for bacteria. You eat, particles of food are left in the
crevices between your teeth, bacteria begin to decompose the
debris and a sticky film forms on the teeth at gum level. This
later hardens as **plaque** and erodes both the tooth enamel
and irritates the gum margin. If the condition is allowed to
escalate, the gum becomes infected and loosens, leaving the
base of the tooth vulnerable to decay.

Sugary foods and drinks are the most dangerous film or plaque-forming agents; ideally you should brush your teeth after each sugared coffee, fruit squash, chocolate bar and biscuit, to prevent the insidious bacterial action. Never suck mints to hide bad breath for the same reason. If you're less than confident, suck a **chlorophyll** tablet. Try to wean yourself off sweets by chewing celery sticks and carrots instead. These exercise the teeth, giving them something to work on, whilst they stimulate saliva to act as a natural mouthwash. But beware of fruit. Most contain a high proportion of natural sugar. So rinse after that apple!

A weekly check with plaque-disclosing tablets shows you just how much has been allowed to build up. The tablets stain the deposits red or blue, so that you can pay special attention to the affected areas and remove the stain and then plaque with it. A thorough brushing at least twice daily (preferably after lunch, too) should prevent serious build-up. Use a toothbrush with rounded nylon tips, medium soft, so that it will clean your teeth without scratching your gums. When the bristles begin to lose their shape, it's time for a new brush. On average, you should renew your brush every two months or so.

Fluoride toothpastes have shown positive results in preventing tooth decay in children and seem a good idea for adults too. Abrasive pastes and powders, however, are frowned upon by dentists, as they may wear away the tooth enamel as well as the stains they're designed to remove. But if your teeth are badly stained by black coffee, red wine or smoking, a gentle brushing with salt is a less fierce method of whitening your teeth again. Talking of whiteness, the colour of your teeth is hereditary and governed by the same factors which determine your bone colour. Yellowish teeth are not necessarily unhealthy or dingy and no amount of brushing and scrubbing can whiten them. To prevent them looking duller than they need, avoid staining agents like those mentioned above and ask your dentist to clean and descale your teeth at your regular six-monthly visits. Dark lipsticks can also make your teeth look dull, so stay with the clearer tones.

There is a right and wrong way to brush your teeth. A quick 'up-and-downer' is totally inadequate for thoroughly removing particles of trapped food. Brush in one direction only to dislodge debris successfully. Starting with the top row of teeth, brush lightly downwards from the gum edges, reaching right round to the back molars. Rinse thoroughly, then use dental floss. Break off around eight inches and wind the ends around the index fingers of both hands, then gently work the floss between each tooth, right up to the gum so that you're actually massaging just under the gum margin. (Be very careful not to 'saw' with the floss as this damages the gum.) Work gently down again. You'll be surprised at the amount of debris even a careful brushing can miss! Dental floss also helps to strengthen the gum margin against the ravages of plaque. Some people prefer Interdens, a softish wooden toothpick, and these too can be effective.

For a model, a good dentist is as valuable an ally as a good hairdresser. Not only is he concerned with the health of your teeth and gums, but he can advise you a great deal on their cosmetic appearance, helping you to achieve as near perfect a smile as possible. Crooked teeth can be filed down and tipped with natural-looking crowns or caps; a filling in an awkward or obvious position can be done with a special cosmetic amalgam so that it won't show. Pick his brains and check out your possibilities. And be conscientious about your regular check-ups.

Keeping fresh at work

A modelling job inevitably means that you will be working closely with others, wearing other people's clothes, and if a make-up artist is present, someone else's make-up. As a two-way protection safeguard, your portable checklist should include:

(1) A spare pair of pants (preferably flesh coloured).
(2) A dark, medium and light pair of tights.
(3) A tampon or mini-pad.
(4) Talcum powder.
(5) Anti-perspirant.
(6) Toothbrush, paste and breath freshener.

8
Top-to-Toe Treatments

Good grooming goes hand in glove with a high standard of hygiene. But whereas hygiene is more intimately concerned with what goes on inside you, grooming is the natural extension to maintain the near perfect façade. Top show, it may be—but keeping your 'upholstery' looking good and well-conditioned is the very essence of a model's physical make-up.

Hand care

Hands play an important role in modelling—and in everyday conversation and expression, come to that. People notice hands. Rough, coarse skin with bitten nails and chipped polish shows a girl up to be dilatory about her appearance and implies a lack of 'polish' in her work. From a model's point of view, bad hands limit her performance in front of the camera. So many shots call for hands as accessories to a 'mood' or expression, and compromising a 'look' in order to hide the model's bad hands can result in an awkward composition.

To encourage nails to grow healthily and keep the cuticles smooth and supple, you must perform a thorough manicure at least once a week. Your equipment consists of:

Cotton wool   Almond oil
Oily polish remover   Leather buffer
A bowl of warm, soapy water   Base coat

Emery boards

Orange sticks

Hand cream

Nail polish

Top coat

Quick-dry spray

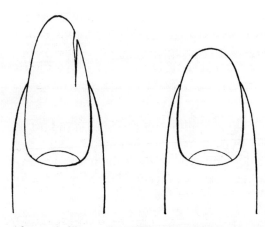

After gentle filing a split can be carefully mended with a special nail glue (see page 77)

(1) Begin your manicure by removing old polish. Soak a nail-sized piece of cotton wool in remover, then place onto each nail. Wait a couple of seconds, then slowly and firmly slide the cotton wool off the nail. Repeat if necessary—but generally you shouldn't need to. This is the least messy way of removing polish!

(2) Shape your nails with the lighter, less abrasive side of the emery board, using light, quick strokes upwards from the sides to the centre. Your ideal is an almond shape, which echoes the gentle curve of your cuticles. Very long, sharp tips are not only unfashionable and unnatural, but encourage the nails to weaken or split at the sides. Always shape your nails when they are dry and not softened by soaking, when they are more likely to tear or flake. Cutting your nails can also tear them, so scissors are best forgotten unless your nails are so long that you need that head-start.

(3) Dip your nails into an eggcup of warmed almond oil, and massage the cuticles. This helps soften the cuticles and prevent the nail itself from drying out in the soapy water to follow.

(4) Soak your fingertips in a bowl of warm, soapy water for around five minutes to soften the cuticles thoroughly and loosen dirt and dead skin under the nail tip. Blot lightly dry with a tissue.

(5) Wrap both ends of an orange stick with a thin coating of cotton wool. Gently ease the tip of the hoof end under the cuticles, working around the base, removing any loose skin. With the pointed end of the orange stick, clean under the nail tip. Never force the cuticle back, or press hard around the nail base. The nail grows from this point and is the only soft, living area of the entire plate. Bruising and damaging here causes ridges and splits when the nail grows further up. Similarly, do not force back the skin under the tips in order to create more 'white' area. Apart from the sheer soreness of torn skin, the nail needs this underlying support. Rinse hands in clear water and pat dry.

(6) Using the leather buffer, gently buff each nail length-wise to improve the circulation, strengthen the nails and give a slight sheen.

(7) Warm a spot of hand cream in the palm of each hand then massage each finger between the thumb and middle fingers of the other hand, travelling firmly from base to tip. Stroke each hand upwards vigorously to stimulate the blood flow to the fingertips. Remove grease from the nails with a cotton-wool-wrapped orange stick dipped in water.

(8) Apply your polish. Paint on the base coat first to prevent the pigment of bright nail polishes staining the nail surface. Apply in two or three slow, firm strokes from base to tip, either side of the nail, then the centre. By the time you have painted both sets of nails, the base should be dry enough to apply the polish. Make sure you have the right amount on your brush. It should be evenly coated so that it remains fluid and sufficiently flexible to coat your nails evenly without blobbing or dragging. Repeat the procedure as for the base coat, then wait a couple of minutes for it to settle. Apply a second coat if the first looks uneven or transparent, then seal the colour with a clear top coat to prevent chipping and make your polish last longer. (Some manufacturers combine base and top coats in one product, which certainly cuts down the

amount of bottles on your dressing table.) Tidy any smudges around the nails with the point of an orange stick wrapped in remover-dampened cotton wool.

Keep your hands in trim and your nail polish intact for as long as possible between manicures by following these guidelines. Always wear **rubber gloves** when using detergents and hot water to prevent the skin and cuticles from drying and the nails from softening and tearing. Use **barrier creams** when doing 'dirty' jobs (like housework or preparing vegetables) to prevent grime and fruit stains engraining themselves into the skin. Rinse hands thoroughly in running water after washing and dry properly. Keep a bottle of **hand cream** by the sink and give your hands a mini-massage, gently stroking back the cuticles with the fleshy part of your fingertips each time you wash your hands. Treat your hands as you would your face—use a cream last thing at night to prevent moisture loss. Keep hands dry, warm and protected by barrier creams and gloves to prevent chapping in cold weather. Never use nails to open tins or cartons, and dial the telephone with a pencil to prevent splitting and breaking.

How to cope with problems

Nail-biting

The ugliest nightmare! Not only does it turn a reasonably graceful pair of hands into stubby paws, but it actually reduces the amount of strong nail area when the nail begins to grow back. You can always tell a reformed nail biter by the proportion of pink to white. As the nail was habitually nibbled further down the 'quick', the eventual re-growth at the tip, although weak and brittle-looking, easily equals the basic pink area.

Lack of 'something to do with the hands' is the common excuse for nervous nibblers, so try occupying them with knitting or even fiddling with a piece of material whilst you're watching television, listening to records, or travelling. Keeping them manicured and coated with nail-strengthening clear varnish is a good deterrent. Avoid bright polishes which draw attention to your stubby nails while they're growing back, but flatter them instead with muted flesh tones or simply clear varnish.

Weak nails

First of all, eating quantities of gelatine cannot strengthen soft nails, nor can it encourage them to grow. However, some people believe that kelp or seaweed supplements from health stores have an effect on both nails and their relations in keratin, hair. Avoid soaking them in very hot water and detergents which dries nails out and causes the keratin layers to separate and peel.

Resign yourself to the fact that you cannot grow your nails to any great length. Keep them well-filed and shaped instead—the shorter they are the longer they are likely to stay intact. Reinforce them with a nail-strengthening product, or an extra-hard strengthening varnish.

Splits and breakages

If a nail snaps off completely you can either replace it temporarily with a false nail (more about those on p. 79) to maintain an even set for a special occasion or, better still, file the rest down to its level. This seems harsh, but in reality nothing looks more ludicrous than one stubby nail amongst a set of near talons.

You can mend a split, however, and save your nail until it has grown far enough to file by using a special nail repair glue. These glues are a slight variation of the all-purpose quick-drying household glues and should be treated with the same amount of caution. Make sure the nail is clean, dry and free from grease; then very carefully flood the split with a small droplet of the glue. Quickly remove any glue from the surrounding finger with polish remover to prevent burning or skin sticking to skin. When the glue has set (a matter of minutes), file flush to the nail surface and apply nail polish to hide the join. The mend will last longer if you file the nail down a little first, to reduce the stress on the tear (see p. 74).

Discoloration

As mentioned above, you can prevent discoloration from nail polish by wearing a protective base coat. But once polish has stained your nails, you'll just have to wait until it grows out as nothing can remove it. Other stains like nicotine, ink, fruit juice and hair colorant may respond to lemon juice or a small amount of hydrogen peroxide solution in the same way as is used for bleaching leg hair. Rinse thoroughly afterwards and apply hand cream. Never use scouring powders or household bleach.

The colour of your nails reflects your state of health. If you can think of no other reason for the discoloration, check with your doctor to set your mind at rest.

Flecks and ridges

The prime cause of any irregularity in the nail is damage to the soft, living base. Knocks and rough treatment around the cuticles cause bumps and flecks, while more serious damage (trapping the nail in a door, say) can cause the nail to grow permanently deformed. Ridges are often caused by scraping the nails instead of using polish remover! Again, ill-health can leave its mark—the effects of 'flu, for example, scarring the nail until it grows out completely, in about three and a half months.

Unfortunately, nothing can remove white flecks. But ridges can be eased by regular buffing and a coating of ridge-filler base to provide a smoother surface for your nail polish. Never attempt to file down ridges as this weakens the nails and may damage them further.

Hangnails

These are often caused by neglecting the cuticles, which cling to the nails and then tear as the nails grow upwards. Do not cut off the cuticle itself as it will grow back tough and more difficult to manicure. Snip away the loose flap of skin only with a sharp pair of nail scissors, then massage hand cream around the nail base.

False nails: when should you wear them?

False nails, used singly, can be a valuable back-up when you break one of your own. But there are drawbacks. False nails generally do look false. Although they come in different shapes and sizes, it's a rare thing to find a set that fits perfectly, moulding itself to your nail's natural curve and looking the same size as your own.

Worn constantly, false nails can hamper the healthy growth of the nails underneath as they block off oxygen and the adhesive may irritate the surrounding skin. Beware also of the artificial nail tips which are popular as salon treatments, as well as generally available in chemists and department stores. These are particularly damaging as they involve the filing and scoring of the nail beneath, to provide a surface to which the nail tip can adhere. In some cases, this treatment causes permanent ridging—much more unsightly than the nails themselves.

However, if you do wish to use false nails, keep them for special occasions only. Ask the sales assistant if she has a tester set that you can 'try on' before you buy them, although you may still have to file them down for a perfect fit. Soak them for five or so minutes in hot water so they become sufficiently malleable for you to bend them to echo your own nail's curve. File the rough edges from your natural nails, then apply a small spot of the adhesive provided to the dry false nail and leave for around thirty minutes. Apply a strip of adhesive to your own nail from base to tip, then fit the false nail and press firmly into place. To remove the nail, apply the solvent provided in the packet under the false nail tip, wait a few seconds, then gently rock the false nail free.

Foot care

Your feet take the weight of your entire body, so it is hardly surprising that their greatest problem is a build-up of hard skin around the heels and balls. Before we go any further, it *is* a good idea to visit a qualified chiropodist every couple of months to have the toughest skin professionally pared away, and to seek advice and treatment for problems like corns and callouses. But there is a lot you can do in between visits to keep your feet in the best possible condition.

It is unfair that these two hard-working appendages are so often neglected. It seems that energy and interest dwindle the further down the body we get. So that when it comes to the feet, a quick scrub with a sponge is all we have time for. But you don't have to be a foot model to have a duty towards these forgotten 'extras'. Summer photographs call for bare legs and sandals—bare feet even. So it pays to keep yours constantly up to scratch.

A pedicure follows virtually the same steps as a manicure, and employs the same equipment with the addition of a pair of nail clippers and **pumice-stone**. You should indulge in a thorough footbath once a week, or carry out the following procedure after a bath when the hard skin is softened:

(1) Work the pumice-stone in circular movements around the damp heels and balls of your feet to slough away the dead, hard skin. Work lightly over any hard skin on the tips of the toes, without scraping the nails themselves.

(2) With an orange stick wrapped in damp cotton wool, ease back the cuticles and clean around the nails as with the manicure mentioned above. Rinse feet and dry briskly with the rough side of a towel. Massage gently in between the toes, drying thoroughly.

(3) Check the length of the nails every three weeks or so. They should be no longer—or shorter—than just covering the tip of the toe beneath. Clip them straight across with the nail clippers. (Do not shape the sides as this encourages in-growing toenails.) Smooth the edges with the fine side of an emery board so that there are no jagged edges to snag tights or cause tears (see page 82).

(4) Squeeze a walnut-sized blob of hand cream or body lotion into the palm of your hand then massage it over each foot, treating each toe individually. Firmly stroke the feet

between both hands from toes up onto your ankles several times to boost circulation and soothe aches.

(5) Remove grease from the toes with a cotton-wool bud soaked in water or polish remover, then apply nail polish, making sure the toes are well separated by firm pads of cotton wool.

Healthy, good-looking feet are vitally dependent on the **shoes** you wear. Comfortable well-fitting shoes are not a luxury: they're a must. Cramped feet are beset with hard, impacted skin, and corns at best, becoming literally deformed with callouses, misshaped toes and fallen arches at worst. As a model, a large part of your life will be spent on your feet, trudging around on appointments and auditions. So good shoes make double good sense for you. Save your trendy high heels for evenings when your feet don't have to take so much punishment.

Your ideal shoe, then, should be slightly longer than your foot and wide enough to allow your toes to lie straight, uncramped, and move freely with the rest of your foot when you walk, but not so loose that you have to grip with your toes to keep your shoes on. A good shoe-shop will still have a foot gauge which you can use as a guide, even though few modern shoes come in any kind of detailed fittings. Choose your heels no higher than two and a half inches so that the weight is not forced down to the ball of your feet and toes. Flat shoes are by far the best as they distribute the weight and so the strain over the entire foot. Never buy shoes without trying them on—and never buy sale shoes that are too small thinking your feet will stretch them. The insult to your feet is no bargain.

Wear cotton or wool socks whenever you can to allow your feet to breathe and move freely, reduce friction and absorb perspiration. Buy them to fit too—undersized tights and socks can cramp your feet as much as too-small shoes.

Whenever you can, exercise and air your feet by going bare-foot, at home, say. Or wear wooden exercise sandals.

Foot problems

Most serious problems are best dealt with by a chiropodist. But you can do your best to prevent them.

Corns or callouses

A corn is a build-up of hard skin which forms a buffer against constant friction. It is not live, and the core is not a root—simply the hardest part of an area of hard skin. Corn plasters are not generally held to be a good idea. Although they soften the corn itself, they may also burn the healthy surrounding skin causing a painful infected area. A chiropodist is the best person to treat the corn. Meanwhile ease the friction by wearing a corn pad which will cushion the area. And leave off the shoes which caused the corn!

In-growing nails

These are sometimes caused by too small footwear forcing the nail into the fleshy padding of the toe itself, although sometimes, due to the natural shape of the nail in proportion to the toe, the flesh can overwhelm the nail. Never cut down sides of the nail, or cut the nail too near the 'quick'.

You can relieve the pain and try to encourage the nail to grow straight by tucking a small amount of cotton wool

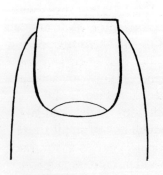

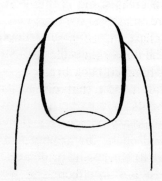

1 First clip toe
   nails straight
   across

2 Prettily rounded
   but too long for
   comfort

under the nail at the sides. But again a chiropodist is the best person for expert treatment.

Athlete's foot

This complaint is highly infectious. So you have a moral obligation to see your doctor and get it cleared up. It's a fungal infection which thrives in warm, moist conditions, attacking the toenails and between the toes, causing the skin to itch and peel.

The treatment is usually a course of anti-fungal tablets, creams and foot powder. Meanwhile, help prevent infection by drying meticulously between your toes, using regular absorbent foot powder if your feet tend to perspire heavily and changing footwear frequently.

Bodyworks

Keeping every part of your body smooth and even-toned is just as important as presenting a fresh, glowing face to the world. Especially when it's the swimwear season! It pays to get into the habit of giving yourself a friction massage each time you take a bath or shower. Combine your washing with the sloughing action of a friction mitt or loofah, paying special attention to knees, elbows, around your heels where the skin creases and is therefore coarsest. Then with lighter pressure, massage the backs of your arms, thighs and but-tocks, chest and shoulders to pep up circulation and slough away the dead skin build-up. Do not neglect your backview. A long-handled back brush is a valuable investment and you will find it isn't that difficult to carry out your massage movements.

Treat greasy or spotty areas on the body—the shoulders, back and chest, for example—as you would your face (see Chapter 8). Cleansing grains are especially easy to use in the bath and are an effective way of treating a problem chest. Steady your hand, though—they are more expensive than a friction mitt or pad. Out of the water, buff yourself vigorously

A back brush can be a valuable investment

dry with the coarser side of a warm towel, gripping it at either end, strapwise, to rub across your shoulders, back, buttocks and thighs. Then pat dry the more delicate skin around your neck, breasts, and abdomen. Treat spotty and greasy areas with the appropriate lotions and creams. Then finish your body-smoothing with a generous helping of moisturising body lotion. Be as lavish with the dry-skin areas as you were firm with the friction mitt. Then slip on your dressing gown while you have breakfast, or do your make-up so that when you finally dress, your skin will have cooled off and the lotion will have settled and won't smear on your clothes.

Coping with unwanted hair

No one likes to see hairy armpits or fuzzy legs, either in a photograph, or for real, especially if your hair is dark and really noticeable. But although body hair is thought to play a role in temperature regulation, it is also argued that its removal is helpful to hygiene—especially in the case of underarm hair which can trap perspiration.

Electrolysis and **diathermy**, which destroy the root of the hair, are the only methods of permanent hair removal. But both can take several courses and as many months to work properly and can leave scars if inexpertly carried out. Generally, extreme measures like these simply aren't necessary. You can keep your body hair in trim yourself with a number of quite straightforward methods.

Shaving

This is probably the most straightforward method of hair removal. It's certainly the quickest—something else you can do in the bath as you need to prepare your skin with soap and the razor with hot water, so that it glides smoothly and shaves evenly and closely. You can also buy electric 'Lady Shavers' which are designed to use on dry skin (never in a bath!) and are portable, to make the process even easier.

There is no truth in the old wives' tale that shaving makes the hair grow back thicker. But because it slices the hair straight across at skin level, in two to three days it grows back rough and stubbly, instead of naturally tapered. Be very careful to keep a steady hand to avoid cutting your skin whilst shaving. Obviously nicks look dreadful on your legs, but they can also be terribly painful and open to infection under your arms.

Creams and lotions

The main advantage of **depilatory** products is that they chemically dissolve the hair just below the skin surface, leaving the skin absolutely smooth and slightly delaying the re-growth. When the hair does grow again—in around three to five days—it is less stubbly than after shaving, having soft, tapered tips. The chemicals themselves can cause a reaction on sensitive skin, so you should always patch test a small area twenty-four hours before you do the whole job.

Creams and lotions are messy, and take time to work—usually ten to twenty minutes, longer if the hair is coarse. But if you leave them on far longer than the time stated on the packet, you are risking irritation. The bikini area at the tops of the legs seems particularly prone to irritation, and may well come up in a rash the day after depilation, so time your treatment so that it won't coincide with a swimsuit assignment!

Waxing

This method has the longest-lasting results because it actually pulls out the hairs at the roots. Therefore, it can take two or three weeks before re-growth appears and the hairs seem fine and tapered. Some people say that in the long-term waxing can destroy the hair root altogether, preventing re-growth. But this can take years of regular treatment, and is by no means the rule.

There are several methods of waxing. Hot wax is the most popular and consists of stroking heated, softened depilatory wax onto the skin with a spatula; then when it has cooled to a putty-like consistency, quickly pulling it off against the direction of the hair growth, so that the hairs are pulled off with it. The process is repeated until the whole area has been treated. The wax can be heated up and reused several times.

Cold wax and resin methods are less of a fuss, as they can be applied straight from the tube onto the skin. Strips of linen are then pressed over the wax, and torn quickly off. Ready-to-use wax strips are based on the same principle, but do not require additional fabric strips. You can wax where you like—under arms, legs, bikini line—but a thoroughly careful job may require the help of a friend.

Waxing *is* painful, even if the pain only lasts for a few seconds, and it is extremely hard to inflict pain willingly on yourself! For this reason, a salon wax is a good investment, especially if you're treating the bikini line. A trained beautician can perform the whole operation quickly and skilfully, causing the minimum pain and irritation. Hopefully, you will even avoid the rash that tugging out tougher hairs can often cause.

Bleaching

If your hairs are very fine or reasonably light and you don't want to have to repeat the performance every few days or so, bleaching renders the hair on legs and arms, for instance, virtually invisible until it eventually falls out and new hair grows (around six weeks). It can also weaken the hairs. The safest way is to use cream bleach preparations from chemists and department stores, and follow the instructions to the letter. Always do a patch-test to prepare for any irritation the bleach may cause on your skin.

After any method of hair removing, calm and soothe the skin by thoroughly removing the product, splash with cold water, then massage on body lotion or baby cream.

9
Face Facts

The most important area of skin for a model—or any young lady worth her fair share of compliments—is the skin on her face. As we have already discussed the healthy cleansing and upkeep of the body skin, let's now extend our thoughts upwards. After all, skin is skin, whichever area it covers. It is only our attitudes to it and uses for it that separate zone from zone.

Facial skin care falls into three categories—the famous cleanse, tone and moisturise routine—with a further 'treatment' section for problem skin.

The only ways in which facial skin differs essentially from body skin are that it is constantly exposed to sunlight, central heating, atmospheric pollution, extremes of heat and cold, and it responds more colourfully to emotion. For this reason, it is even more important to maintain a healthy respect for the skin's own protective devices.

Cleansing

This is especially apparent when it comes to cleansing the skin. In order to maintain a soft, glowing skin surface, you must, of necessity, remove a certain amount of the cosmetically unattractive defence ingredients—oil and keratin. Neither looks good on bare skin or under make-up. Oil causes make-up to melt or 'sweat' and attracts dust and grime from the air; a build-up of keratin results in flaking skin, and gives the complexion a dull grimy appearance. Yet both do their bit in preventing moisture loss from the skin beneath the 'horny layer'. So again, it's a question of balance, the ideal being to please ourselves cosmetically, without disrupting the skin itself.

Soap and water make Enemy Number One for some girls' faces. As with the body skin, there is the risk that harsh soaps may dissolve natural oils. With extra greasy skins, or faces with an oily centre panel, there's an added complication. The skin thinks it's doing the right thing by pumping out all the sebum. If you remove it from the surface, the skin responds by quickly replacing it—just like the greasy hair syndrome discussed in Chapter 10. If you like to wash your face, cleansing bars which are acid-balanced are your answer as they are formulated to cleanse without disturbing the skins' protective mantle. Wash with tepid water, then rinse thoroughly with clear, running water. Pat or gently buff with a soft towel. The massage action of washing helps dislodge dead keratin cells, frees blocked pores and generally cleans the skin of a build-up of make-up. Even dry skin may need an occasional—say once weekly—wash to prepare the skin thoroughly for moisturising treatments later and to stimulate the circulation.

As an alternative to the cleansing bars, some manufacturers include 'foaming' or rinsable cleansers in their range. These are creams which you stroke onto dry skin, then work into a lather with water before you eventually rinse off. The third option is the cream cleanser family, which requires no water and so carries the least risk of dehydrating the skin.

Oil itself (usually paraffin or a derivative) is the active ingredient which removes make-up, although some lighter-textured lotions formulated for greasy skins maybe virtually oil-free. Waterproof products like eyeshadows and especially mascaras need oil-based cleansers to shift them gently and completely. Scrubbing your eyes with any other form of cleanser is futile and can stretch and irritate the thin skin around the eyes.

Masks or face packs are pleasant once-weekly 'brightening' treatments which remove dead cells from the skin's surface and improve the texture by temporarily tightening the skin and pores. They also bring the blood to the surface and so give you a fresh outdoors look. There are several kinds. The clay or kaolin-based masks work as oil absorbers for greasy skins and are usually left on until they whiten or dry, then you rinse off. Brush-on, peel-off masks are the most fun. You literally smooth them on either with a brush or your fingers, leave them until their rubbery substances have set and then peel them off—in one piece if you're lucky! They are usually formulated for normal to oily skins.

The very mildest masks are the moisturising or soothing packs for dry skins. Much creamier in texture, these are simply left for a stated amount of time, then gently removed with damp cotton-wool pads or splashed off with water. Always avoid the eye area when using any mask and follow the instructions to the letter. If your skin stings more than the usual tingling sensation, rinse off immediately, and apply liberal helpings of moisturiser.

It is not a good idea to try a new mask or 'home facial' just before a special occasion, or the night before an assignment. The extra stimulus may cause the skin to break out in a rash or spots.

Toning

Toners are useful not only for calming the skin after cleansing, but for removing every last trace of the cleanser itself. The active ingredient is usually alcohol, the concentration of which varies from product to product, according to the skin type for which it is formulated. Oily skins should opt for an astringent toner; if you have a skin with an oily centre panel you should wipe that zone only with an astringent and use a milder tonic for the drier cheek areas.

Skin 'fresheners' contain the least alcohol (sensitive-skin products may in fact contain none at all) and are best for dry skins. Never overdo your toning, though, as it can dry the skin too much. If you think yours is too strong (your skin tingles say, or comes up in blotches) dilute it with water or use on a premoistened cotton wool ball.

Special problems

Special problems need special treatments. Paradoxically, the skin type which causes the most heartache is the oily type— even though it has a much better chance, long-term, of staying line-free and young looking. However, spots, acne and blackheads aren't going to boost anyone's confidence or contribute much to a career in front of the camera.

Spots are caused by the oil-glands becoming blocked. The first stage is the hardened plug of sebum, which, when exposed to the air, undergoes a chemical reaction and darkens. (Blackheads are nothing to do with dirty skin.) As the blockage builds up, the sebum bursts through the wall of the duct and infects the surrounding tissue. Thus, a spot is born.

The first step in treating spotty skin is the preventive measure of keeping the pores free. Blackheads can be loosened by massage with gritty cleansing grains, an abrasive nylon pad or, more gently, a cosmetic cleansing brush, then carefully eased out with clean, tissue-wrapped fingers while the skin is still warm. (Allow the skin to cool, and the pores will contract.) Steaming the skin is *not* a good idea. It may well open the pores, but it involves too much moisture loss from the skin as it sweats in the attempt to cool itself. Never force a blackhead as this can cause bruising to the surrounding tissue or hasten a spot. The next stage, if a spot has already formed, is to dry it out and peel away the build-up of keratin which is contributing to the blockage.

There is a profusion of spot-drying products on the market, usually based on resorcinol, salicylic acid, benzoyl peroxide and sulphur. But be careful where you apply them. Keep your spot-checks topical, and the lotions as far as possible from affecting the normal surrounding skin.

Acne is a complaint apart from the more usual spottiness and should be treated by a doctor and not by yourself. It is caused by the upsurge of hormonal activity—especially androgen, the male hormone, present in both sexes—around the time of puberty. There is no foundation in the old wives' tales that chips and chocolates trigger off acne (though from a figure, if not a face-saving angle, both are best eaten with caution). In addition to excess sebum production, heavy make-up is also a contributory factor to pore blockage. So keep make-up as light and free as possible (see Chapter 11 for more advice) and always remove model make-up after a job, before you go home.

Moisturising

Moisturising is the last stage of your skin care routine. You are in effect attempting to replace some of the moisture and defence that you removed during the cleansing process. But do not believe any wild claims that these creams will introduce ingredients which resemble the skin's own very effective barrier, since the base of the epidermis prevents most substances penetrating to the heart of the skin—the dermis itself.

Any product which says it can supply reinforcements to cells and substances like collagen is merely generating wishful thinking. The most a moisturiser can do is to plump up the horny layer with water and leave a slick of oil on the surface to try to keep it in there. Moisturisers, then, are composed essentially of oil and water. It is how these two components are formulated in relation to each other that determines which cream is best for your skin type.

Oily skins may need a moisturiser, especially before a foundation with a built-in moisturising agent. If your skin is only slightly oily, you may need a thin film of a non-greasy oil-in-water lotion over the central panel where the concentration of sebum glands is the greatest, then a second helping over the drier throat and cheek areas.

Dry skins should opt for the richer water-in-oil creams which are more effective at preventing moisture loss as they contain more oil.

A young skin should not need extra heavy overnight creams. Unless your skin really is dry, a helping of your regular moisturiser after cleansing last thing should be sufficient to control moisture loss until the morning.

Moisturisers work best after being warmed in the palm of

your hand. Dot over the forehead, cheeks, nose and chin. Then, with fingertips of both hands touching at the centre forehead, begin your massage by stroking up to the hairline, then out to the temples with firm but gentle movements. Circular pressure on the temples helps to relax and soothe you. Stroke the fingertips lightly down the nose several times, then working upwards, massage in small circular movements either side of the nostrils. Move outwards and upwards across the cheeks towards the temples. Fingers together at the chin's central point, stroke firmly outwards and up around the mouth corners. Tilting your head right up, stroke upwards over your throat with alternate hands. (You can also use this massage when cleansing your face, especially when using creams.) Blot off any excess moisturiser that remains when you've finished your massage by lightly pressing a tissue over your forehead, either sides of your nose and chin.

A word of warning about the eye area. Because the skin there is thinner and is bolstered by less underlying fatty tissue, it is generally drier and more delicate than the skin on the rest of your face. Keep toners—especially the astringent ones—away from this zone and be extra gentle with moisturisers. Some products—especially those containing lanolin—can cause the eyes to puff up. So be sparing. A mere spot, gently stroked over the lids and under-eyes is sufficient. Special eye creams are generally not so very different from basic moisturisers, so save your money. It's better spent elsewhere. If your eyes do swell, place cotton wool soaked in chilled eye lotion over each closed lid and relax for as long as you can spare. (A good tip after a sleepless or tearful night, also!)

Lastly, always take your own set of cleanser, toner and moisturiser on 'sessions' with you. Tell a make-up artist if your skin is sensitive and likely to react to any brand or formula. If this is the case, as well as your own skin-care products, take along your own foundation to act as a barrier between your skin and 'foreign' cosmetics. Make sure also that the make-up artist has thoroughly cleaned his or her brushes after the last job. The majority are meticulous. But it's still worth a check. After all, it's *your* face in their hands.

10
Hair Sense

Your hair is the most important part of your 'look'—the 'make or break' factor if you like. Time was when models could rely on a selection of wigs to achieve their various images. But today's look is natural, casual and healthy, and that's something only *real* hair can achieve. Like your skin, your hair is a barometer, reflecting whatever goes on inside you. If you're in the peak of condition, then your hair is shining and bouncy. If you're under the weather, tired or under stress, then your hair bears this out by becoming dull and lacklustre.

A well-balanced diet plays a vital role in your hair's health. (Your daily good food checklists in Chapter 6 contain all the elements needed for healthy hair growth.) But just as important is your treatment of your hair from the outside. To manage it and keep it in tip-top condition, you need to understand your hair, what it is and how it grows.

Having said that your hair is so responsive to your state of health, it seems a contradiction to say next that visible hair—the hair above the scalp—is as dead as your fingernails. In fact, the hair shaft is composed of scales of **keratin**—the same horny substance of which your nails are made.

Hair life and growth happen deep in the skin below the scalp. Until it reaches the surface, the young hair is surrounded by the **follicle**—a tightly-fitting 'tunnel', the bulbous bottom of which houses the hair root. Here cells rapidly reproduce, making the hair grow about half an inch a month—the fastest growth-rate in the entire body! (One explanation of why hair is so quick to register ill health!)

Hair **colour** is determined by hereditary factors and created,

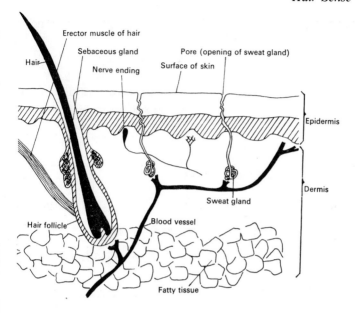

Anatomy of a hair follicle (from *Human Biology Made Simple*)

also around the root area, by **melanocytes**—the pigment-producing cells which deposit colour in the growing cells. Connected to each follicle is a **sebaceous**, or oil-producing, gland. This gland pumps oil into the follicle and up onto the hair shaft, coating and smoothing down the scaly layers of the outer keratin. It is this sebum which ideally gives hair its sheen and holds moisture in the shaft, enabling it to maintain its springy elasticity. Less ideally, it makes life miserable for a girl with over-greasy hair.

Hair does eventually stop growing, and falls out when pushed by a newly forming hair beneath. It's quite usual for your hairbrush to collect anything up to 100 hairs daily! The lifespan of each hair varies. Some girls can grow hair long enough to sit on, quite steadily over a period of six years or more, whilst others 'stick' at a mere two years' shoulder-length growth. Growth-rate also depends on the time of the year, stepping up in summer and slowing down in winter, which could well account for a larger than usual crop of hairs gleaned by the brush in spring, as the elderly hairs 'moult'.

Nothing can speed growth or increase the amount of hairs growing on your head, but you can make the very best of what you *have* and persuade it to perform for you by following a sensible hair-care strategy based on respect for its own character.

How to get the best from your hair

There are three golden rules of hair care: keep it clean, conditioned and in shape. We'll deal with the first two first.

A shampoo's job is a delicate issue

On the one hand, a shampoo's function is to rid your hair of dust, dead cells, stale gels and lotions, build-up of hairspray or any other preparation you've used; but it should do all this without completely stripping your scalp of its natural oils, or seriously disturbing its protective acid mantle. That is why it is absolutely essential to find a mild, non-detergent, acid-balanced shampoo which has some respect for your scalp's condition. Thankfully, manufacturers have increasingly introduced pH (acid/alkali) balanced products into their ranges. Look for a factor of around 4 to 5 to be as near as possibly compatible to your scalp.

Don't fall into the trap of thinking that baby shampoo is the mildest thing going! It's formulated to keep a baby's scalp free of 'cradle cap'—a scurvy build-up of oil and keratin. Frequent use on your own scalp may prove too searching.

A conditioner's role is protective

Conditioner replaces any oils which may have been removed in the shampooing process, coating the hair shaft, and smoothing down the keratin scales so that your hair looks sleek and shiny. It also acts as a buffer between your hair and potential damage (like the drying effects of heated rollers and curling tongs), whilst helping it to retain its resilience and elasticity come set or high styling. Lastly, and equally important, a conditioner helps to prevent moisture loss from the hair shaft and scalp.

The right way to wash your hair

Now you know who your allies are, it's important to know how to use them. You can't expect peak performance from even the best of products if a lightning lather in the bath followed by a fleeting head plunge is all the chance you give them! What goes on, by and large, must come off. And for that you need a limitless supply of clear, running water, preferably from a shower head or rubber spray attachment.

Step 1. Brush your hair thoroughly, head down, to loosen dead cells and the build-up of hair products.

Step 2. Set the taps to run tepid water and wet your hair, lifting up the underneath to make sure it's saturated.

Step 3. With the palm of your hand, smooth about a soupspoonful of shampoo over your entire hair surface, then massage gently into the roots with your fingertips, working over your scalp. Rub hair between both palms to distribute the lather to the tips.

Step 4. Spray rinse until the water runs clear and no trace of shampoo remains; then gently blot excess moisture from your hair with a soft towel.

Step 5. Smooth a good palmful of conditioner over your head; then massage your scalp with your fingertips. With a wide-toothed comb, very gently distribute the conditioner to the hair tips, adding a touch more conditioner if necessary.

Step 6. Make sure that no trace of conditioner is left by running your fingers through your hair whilst spraying, to help free and flush away any trapped preparation. You are now ready to towel dry and style.

How to solve your problems

Above are the general guidelines for your shampoo and condition routine. Some hairtypes, however, need special treatment.

Greasy hair

Try not to be too hard on it. Overzealous shampoos may initially rid you of the glut of oil, but they can also stimulate your scalp into compensating for its losses by pumping out even more, creating a vicious circle.

If you have to wash your hair daily, use a small amount of a mild shampoo, followed by an oil-free conditioner. Dry shampoos help to absorb oil in between shampoos. Avoid scalp stimulation through over-brushing, and cut down on fatty foods like butter, cheese, fried foods and meats.

Dry hair

Use a richer, cream shampoo and conditioner, and wash no more than twice a week. An excellent treatment is to comb warm olive or almond oil through dry hair, then wrap in hot towels and leave for a couple of hours before shampooing. A little conditioner or treatment cream massaged into the tips revives very dry hair in between shampoos.

A course of taking cod or halibut liver oil tablets may help to replace the gloss, whilst supplying the hair with valuable vitamin A. Gentle scalp massage also helps stimulate sebum production and blood circulation which supplies nutrients to the scalp and hair roots.

Fine hair

Only very recently have hair-care manufacturers come up with some real help: shampoos and conditioners containing thickening agents to coat temporarily individual hairs, creating more bounce and texture. Setting gels and mousses also add bulk, help fine hair stand up for itself, and curb its fly-away tendencies.

Coarse hair

Very thick, especially frizzy, hair can be difficult to style and look deadly dull, as the curlier your hair, the less it reflects the light. It may also be brittle, so conditioning is doubly essential. Treat as for dry hair, making sure you thoroughly comb the conditioner right through to the tips to keep up the gloss.

Dandruff

First of all, are you sure it *is* dandruff, and not simply a scurf build-up from inadequate rinsing, or excess hairspray? Real dandruff is excess flakes of keratin produced in self-defence by an irritated scalp. A prime irritant is over-shampooing with highly alkaline shampoos. *The antidote is a mild acid-balanced shampoo, gently massaged into the scalp, then thoroughly rinsed away.*

Medicated shampoos, or selenium-based applications, are not recommended. They can irritate the scalp further. If your problem does not respond to your own treatment or your scalp is sensitive, tender or bleeds, see your doctor.

Giving nature a nudge

As we have already found, there is nothing you can do to make your hair grow faster, or indeed thicker. But you *can* create illusions of fullness by what the professionals call 'processing'—colouring and perming. Colorants come in many formulae and are used in various ways to achieve different effects.

Permanent colour

This has the power to change your hair shade completely, even from black to blonde, or vice versa. The chemicals in the solution penetrate each hair shaft, removing the pigment at the core and replacing it with the new colour which stays until it's cut off. For this reason, as your hair grows, your natural shade will show through at the roots, so regular re-touching is vital if your 'borrowed' shade is to look natural.

There is a pitfall with root retouching. Unless it is done by a professional, or someone with a steady hand and plenty of experience, there is a tendency to re-dye too far up the hair on top of the previous colorant. If done repeatedly, this can produce patchy variation in tone and, worse, badly dry out the hair itself, causing it to become dangerously brittle.

Bleaches

Bleaches come into the 'permanent' category as once the solution has 'stripped out' your natural colour, your hair stays lighter until it's cut. Any product which lightens your hair contains bleach, whether it merely 'lifts' you a touch lighter from mouse to honey, or goes the whole hog and makes a Monroe of you. Going from dark to light may take two stages: from brunette to red, then on to blonde.

Highlights and lowlights

These are permanent tints or bleaches selectively applied onto sections or strands of hair, giving light and depth to enhance your natural shade. Hairdressers use them to 'support' their hairstyles, the lighter tones emphasising the crests of curls, or the highspot of a wave, say, whilst the deeper tints by contrast give the illusion of shape and substance. Alternatively, a combination of high and lowlights—sometimes as many as six at a time—can be applied to the whole head. Subtly based around your own colour, they usually give a convincing impression of thickness to dull or fine hair, without such an obvious 'root' problem when they begin to grow out. Of course, they used simply to be called 'streaks', but as you can imagine advanced hairdressing techniques have given them a much more sophisticated role, and names to go with it.

Semi-permanent colours

This cannot drastically change your natural shade as they contain no penetrating chemicals. Instead they cling to the outer hair layers, enhancing and richening your own tone. A honey-blonde tint, for example, simply would not register on dark brown hair. But on fair hair, a warm golden tone would take the place of what could have been just a dingy-looking blonde.

Most semi-permanent colours are formulated with a conditioner to 'polish' the finished product and add to the glossy illusion. They wash out gradually over a period of around six to eight shampoos.

Wash-out tints

These are colours you shampoo in—and out again the next time you wash your hair. Like semi-permanent tints, they have no power to change your own shade, as most are vegetable and not chemical dyes, but temporarily enhance it by lightly coating the outer hair layer. Sometimes called 'toners' they are good at refreshing old permanent colours which have turned dull or brassy. Blondes may have fun with 'crazy colours'—rainbow tints like pink and blue, painted or sprayed on for parties or photographic sessions, then, thankfully, washed completely away afterwards.

Henna

If you can cope with the sheer mess of hennaing, along with wash-out tinting, it's probably the safest method of colouring your hair. Henna is a vegetable powder which traditionally colours brown hair a very rich red, whilst it is said to condition at the same time. It is also mixed with other natural colorants to enrich black hair and even medium-blonde hair. But it's not advisable for use on very fair hair, as it tends to tint it orange.

The powder is mixed with water, then the 'mud' is combed through the hair. Heat activates the henna, so be prepared for around an hour's session under hot towels or a hood dryer. The colour lasts almost as long as a permanent tint, gradually fading with time. You may have a re-growth problem, so re-apply at the roots only when retouching, to avoid build-up of colour at the tips.

Permanent waves

'Perms' actually alter the structure of the hair by rearranging the keratin scales, then remoulding them into a new pattern. And so a curl is born. Quite how curly your hair will be depends on the strength of the perming solution and the size of the 'rods' or rollers used. Tight perms call for small rods, whilst looser waves which may suit longer hair, say, come from much larger rollers.

Like tinting, perming has become so versatile and sophisticated, a hairdresser can fit a particular technique to your individual hair style and texture. In the first place, the solution itself is much less harsh than it used to be. Thanks to the addition of built-in conditioning agents, perming is a much safer proposition for fine, limp hair—exactly the type which most needs that extra bounce but used to run the highest risk of dry, brittle locks.

Results nowadays are much more natural, too, the emphasis being on fullness, bounce, and what hairdressers call 'movement'. Fast taking over from the wash-and-wear cascade of curls popular for longer layered hair is **'root perming'**, which treats the base of the hair only, giving a lift and a slight bend as opposed to a complete curl. **'Weave perming'** takes this idea a stage further, by treating every alternate section of hair to achieve a casual, tousled look.

All perms work best on layered hair. The sheer weight of very long strands drags the curls out of place on all parts of the hair but the tips.

Straightening is the reverse of perming—the same chemicals are used—but generally the process is more 'severe' and can badly weaken your hair, especially if it's the very tight African type. Thankfully, straightening is going out of fashion and being replaced by more creative and inventive styles tailor-made for Afro hair. A trip to a salon specialising in Afro and Asian hairstyling will convince you it's far more 'trendy' and attractive to go with your hair's own texture than try to force it into something it most certainly is not.

Unless your hair is naturally greasy, you might also find that perming or permanent colouring leaves your hair drier than before. Change then to a richer, cream shampoo and a conditioner specially formulated for 'processed' hair. It's also wise to remember that any type of processing, no matter how mild, does affect your hair's natural structure. To avoid disasters like weak and brittle hair, dried out and patchy in both colour and texture, you must ask a professional hair-dresser to treat you with suitable permanent colour or waves. He will be able to assess how your hair will react to the chemical processes far better than you can. But if you're tinting at home, it's wise to do a 'patch test' twenty-four hours in advance by painting a very small amount of the solution in the inside crook of your arm, to check that your skin will not have an allergic reaction to the product.

Choosing equipment

A good, all-round grounding in an assortment of styling techniques is your key to versatile hair. Using the right equipment is the way to a really professional-looking finish. Even something as basic as choosing the right brush and comb for your hair type makes all the difference.

All hair types should be extremely wary of brushes and over-brushing. Quite contrary to the '100 strokes a day' lore, you should brush your hair only sufficiently to free it gently of daily dust, dead cells and tangles and stop once the brush glides easily through and your hair looks smooth and groomed. Over-brushing stimulates the oil-glands, making greasy hair even more of a problem as it also spreads the oil.

Choose a brush whose bristles have rounded tips so that they cannot scratch your scalp or tear and split the hairs themselves. Avoid natural bristles, however nice they look—they are usually far too hard and sharp.

Rubber-cushioned brushes with rubber or nylon bristles are the easiest to keep clean, and more flexible for gentle styling.

Wide-tooth or afro combs, as the names imply, are specially for very coarse or tightly curly hair. The longer teeth mean you can lift the hair up away from the scalp, making the style look bouncier and fuller.

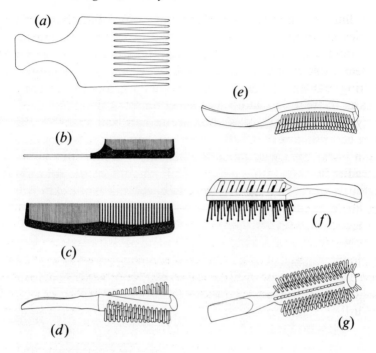

Hair implements: (*a*) Wide tooth or Afro comb; (*b*) Tail comb;
(*c*) Regular comb; (*d*) Semi-radial brush; (*e*) Short bristle brush;
(*f*) Vent angle brush; (*g*) Radial brush

Tail combs are fine-tooth combs with a slim metal rod at one end for lifting sections of hair before blow-drying or roller setting. Use the tail also to lift accurately or coax 'details' into place without disturbing the rest of the style.

Regular combs. Those with larger, wider-spaced teeth at one end, phasing through to fine teeth at the other are useful for most hair types. Use the larger end initially to ease through the hair, then the fine end to get a really smooth even finish.

Semi-radial brushes are the best for smooth blow-drying, as they either straighten or wave your hair, depending on the angle you tilt them. Most hairdressers use these. Choose one with well-spaced bristles for the best results.

Short-bristle brushes, as you might imagine, give a smooth, close finish to short hair because of their more densely spaced bristles. Clean them regularly as they do tend to be the greatest hair-traps.

Vent angle brushes. Those with well-spaced, quite gappy-looking bristles are best for smoothing the tangles out of wet hair as they are less likely to drag or overtax the hair's elasticity. Some even have bulbous-tipped bristles to make them even gentler. Use them, too, for giving extra bounce and lift when blow-drying very fine hair, or styling long hair.

Radial brushes with a completely circular base are for styling curls when blow-drying. The larger the brush, of course, the larger the curls.

Electric brushes do the same job as the manual ones, but blow warm air through the bristles. They are the easiest way to blow-dry your hair, as they leave one hand free to control your hair as you blow. The best ones have a choice of brush and comb attachments for different effects.

Curling tongs, or 'styling wands', can curl or straighten hair. A section of hair, wound spiral fashion around the barrel, held for a second, then released, gives a ringlet effect to long hair, and a curl to short or layered hair. Sliding the barrel down the hair section, held by the clip attachment, straightens. **Heated styling brushes** are like tongs, but with short, rigid bristles around the barrel. They are used to give bounce and larger curls and control coarse, wildly curly hair. Use both appliances on dry or barely damp hair.

Hairdryers are the other partners in the blow-drying team. The best have two speed or heat settings, dual voltage for travelling, a detachable nozzle for concentrated or wider air distribution and are lightweight and easy to handle. Travel dryers should also fold up neatly and take up the minimum space in your bag. Permed or naturally curly heads should look for dryers with special attachments that distribute the air over a much wider area to simulate gentle, natural heat. If you take your dryer or rollers abroad make sure your adaptor is right for the local electricity supply.

Heated rollers set hair quickly into curls and give hair a basic body and bounce for further styling later. It's worth investing in the sets which also condition as, like all electrical stylers, they tend to dry your hair. Wrapping tissue around the rollers helps buffer and protect your hair, but of course, the hair takes longer to set. Most manufacturers now make mini travel sets which ease the burden considerably. Use heated rollers on dry or slightly damp hair.

Six styling tricks

The following styles work best on freshly washed hair, dampened with a blow-dry or setting lotion. The lotion will help the style to stay in longer and buffer your hair from humid atmospheres which could make it frizz or simply 'drop'.

Blow-drying

For even, thorough results, you must blow-dry your hair in sections. Divide your head into four by making a parting with a tail comb from your forehead over your crown to the nape of your neck, then another at the back of your head from ear to ear. Lift the two sections above the back parting, twist into individual ropes and pin out of the way. Collect half of the bottom hair, by lifting it away from the head from underneath, over a semi-radial brush, direct the hair-dryer into the brush (*but keep the nozzle at least six inches away*) whilst you slowly move down the hair section from roots to tips. Repeat until the section is completely dry; then work on the other half of the bottom section. Unpin the hair above the parting, divide it into half by making another parting across the crown from in front of the ears. Comb the front section forward, then dry the back two sections.

Now the back is dry, divide the two front halves into two, then blow-dry each section, angling the brush slightly back from the face. Finish off by brushing through right off the face, then tossing your head forward and back again to let your hair settle naturally. For a curlier or more wavy look, use a complete radial brush, slowly turning it as you move down each section.

Roller setting

Divide off hair section by section, holding each one right out straight from your head. Hold the roller against the tip, then firmly roll around until all the hair is collected and the roller sits snugly against your scalp without tugging at the roots. Secure with a pin against the direction of the roller. The size of the roller, naturally, determines the size curl you'll get. The direction you wind it determines whether the curl will flick up or down. The length of your hair determines how curly or bouncy the result will be.

Rollers really do work best on medium layered hair. If you want a really long-lasting set, roll your hair onto ordinary foam-cushioned rollers, and leave overnight. Heated roller styles do 'drop' more quickly, as the dry hair you're working with is not nearly so easy to persuade as wet hair, and tends to revert to normal.

Pin curling

For this technique you need the larger metal hairdressing clips to hold the curls firmly in place. Pin curling is best for achieving wispy tendrils around the hairline to offset an off-the-face style, say. Section off thinnish strands of hair and wind around the tip of your finger. Gently ease off your finger and pin flat with clips.

Rag-setting

A useful style on holiday for longer hair, when you've no electrical gadgets or bulky rollers. Make one to two inch sections of hair all over your head and twist into 'ropes', holding them at the tips. Let the ropes coil back on themselves by slowly lowering your hand to your head, without letting go of the hair. Tie the tips to their bases with the rags and leave until the hair is thoroughly dry. Brush out and you've a natural, slightly tousled effect.

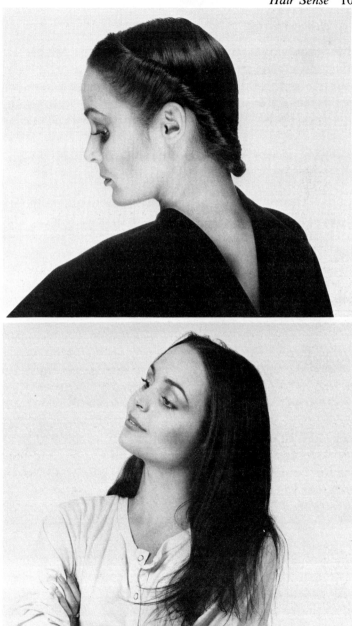

Medium long hair gives any model girl an advantage.
Here top hairdresser, Stephen Way of New Bond Street, London, shows
four contrasting styles on Sue Blackie

Pipe-cleaner setting

Another holiday bonus, for medium-length hair. Simply wind your sections around the individual pipecleaners, spiralling from one end to the other, then bend them into a loop, with the tips facing away from the scalp. When dry, brush through for a casual wavy look.

Plait-setting

A very effective style for all-one-length hair is to plait small sections all over the head, then leave overnight until thoroughly dry. Combed out, you've a wild, crinkly look which stands out from the head, making your hair look wonderfully thick.

Making your choice

Well, now you know the options, which style is right for *you*? Having thrown that question open, it seems unfair to start making restrictions. But realistically, your career must limit the lengths to which you dare go. High fashion styles—however they may suit you personally—are not for you. As a model, they are far too restricting, and allow you only one 'look' and that's that. Fine, if you're an established model who has already built up a clientèle who respect, and book, you for your individuality. But for the girl who's starting out, a cut which lends itself to a good selection of styles for the various different 'looks' you'll be taking on is more of a necessity than an option. And that generally means a slightly layered style, falling somewhere between the jawline and shoulders, which can perform at least the three basic choices of straight, curly and up.

An example of an extremely versatile cut (although maybe not exploited to the full by its celebrated owner) is the style immortalised by the Princess of Wales. Imagine it at shoulder-length, for its full potential. As well as the basic blow-dry style, because of the layers round the sides, it can be tonged into face-framing curls; gathered into side rolls with combs;

knotted into a chignon at the nape; set on large rollers for body, then backcombed on top for extra height and a touch of wild glamour; slicked back off the face with gel, the back tied tightly out of sight in a small bun so that it looks short and sporty; tonged all over for wavy fullness and width. That's six looks in one—and a hairdresser could no doubt dream up more variations.

Your hairdresser

Your hairdresser, in fact, can turn out to be your greatest ally, so it's important to stay with one very good stylist and build up a rapport. Avoid salons who churn out styles like sausage-machines and try to book your appointments when there's the least rush so that your person can give you his undivided concentration. (If you have to book a Saturday appointment, the first one of the morning is best, before the insidious build-up of lateness and panic escalates and the energy of all concerned has diminished.)

Before your hair is washed, your stylist should study your hair, its texture and condition so that he can assess its possibilities. He should take into account your face shape and, more than that, the balance of your hair with the rest of your body. He may even wish to do a preliminary 'dry' cut to obtain a rough outline. You should feed him with all relevant information—your problems, your ideals, how your hair actually behaves from day to day, which products you normally use and their effects.

The *last* thing a hairdresser will want from you is a magazine cutting of your 'dream' style. People's hair varies vastly. The style which looks so perfect on the model in the picture may not suit your particular hair type or face shape and stylists get headaches trying to explain this.

They also know—and so, eventually will you—that those immaculate hairdressing pictures don't just happen with ten minutes under the heated rollers and a quick toss of the head. All the tricks and illusions in the business have probably been used to give that rich, glossy full-blown head of hair. It most likely took a day to achieve, and the model had a raging headache under all the 'cement' holding the style intact.

It works both ways though. You'll need to establish in no uncertain terms that you are not the guinea-pig for your hairdresser's cutting technique or the style he thought up in the bath last night. But let him advise you. Pick his brains—watch him as he styles your hair and don't be afraid to grill him with questions, or ask him to watch as you have a go with the dryer yourself. He's the one who can teach you—so use him well.

Once you both know what he's going to do never be shy to ask how much it will cost. Not asking can be an unintended way of making your hair curl when the bill comes!

Some salons operate a discount scheme for models, or do your hair for free if you agree to become one of their 'house models' and are available for shows, seminars and publicity photographs. This give-and-take system is especially useful if your style maintenance entails regular processing which could otherwise prove hard on the purse. It's also a good way of building up experience and photographs for your portfolio.

Many girls with tight budgets are tempted by the 'Model Nights' at hairdressing schools. Fair enough; you may well know someone who had a marvellous cut for next to nothing. But remember that if you do go along, you're very much the guinea-pig, and the standards of the trainee stylists vary. Although the very best thing about hair is that it does grow, it also takes its time. A slip of the scissors by the trainee could mean that you don't work for a while.

Your hair at work

When you get a booking, if the client hasn't given your agency details of how they want you to arrive with your hair, then your instructions will probably be 'clean face, clean hair', ready for make-up artist and hairdresser at the studio. Most hairdressers prefer to work on freshly washed hair. But does yours style better the *day after* it's washed? Whether you prepare it the night or the morning before, don't forget a generous helping of conditioner. On session, your hair will be bombarded with tortuous treatments—anything from curling tongs to hairspray—all taxing its resilience. So give it some self-defence.

Be prepared also, to meet the unforeseen. Your emergency checklist should include:

(1) Your regular shampoo and conditioner. Decant them into small plastic bottles for travelling or use sachets if available.

(2) Bonded elastic by the yard (from department stores) to tie your hair back without damaging the cuticle.

(3) A selection of hairslides, combs, grips, pins and ribbons.

(4) Your favourite setting gel or lotion.

(5) A hairspray that brushes out easily, travel size.

(6) A clean brush and comb (soak them overnight in warm washing-up solution to dissolve grease and preparations).

(7) A lightweight travel dryer.

(8) A small set of heated rollers.

(9) Curling tongs.

(10) Tissues to wrap around the hairdressers' heated rollers for hygiene's sake.

11
Model Make-up

Every girl should learn how to make up properly, whether she plans a career in front of the camera or behind a desk. At its most basic, make-up enhances your natural features, playing up your good points and fibbing about those not so good, whilst it rounds off your total look, and acts as an accessory to your clothes and hair. At its most extreme, it is quite blatantly a mask. By the sheer skill of illusion, make-up can remould your features, transforming a basically average face into a stunningly glamorous work of art.

A model's make-up bag is her ticket to versatility—that vital ingredient of a successful career. A girl with only one look could well find that after brief, although perhaps intense popularity, she ceases to be fashionable and bookings fall off. One of the qualities agents look for is a face that can 'take make-up'. That usually means even (but, surprisingly, not too distinguished) features, which respond like a blank canvas to brushes and, most important, to the clients' whims.

For a model, then, make-up is divided into two main categories: for herself and for other people. Your own face is the one you wear when you're not in front of a camera; putting it bluntly, it's the *real* you. The second category is fantasy. The basic principles of make-up technique still apply, but once you're 'on show', whether you're making up to a Hasselblad or a catwalk audience, everything becomes exaggerated. With the intensity of the lights and the distance between you and beholder (not to mention the printing processes of magazines) your friendly basic make-up just wouldn't stand a chance.

But a sense of occasion is important when you're making up. One of the most common mistakes made by make-up students and 'freshmen' models alike is to plaster on the paint *outside* the studio. In the cold light of day, even if it is exquisitely applied, heavy make-up looks grotesquely unnatural. Even on appointments, it's best to keep your make-up to a natural-looking minimum. (Some agents suggest mascara and lipgloss only.) You may think you're demonstrating your immense prowess as a '*visagiste*', but the clients would rather see your skin and features as they really are and judge for themselves. After all, you have your portfolio to show off your potential.

Whatever the type of make-up, though, the same basic rules apply:

(1) Choose your light. Daytime make-up is best put on in daylight, which is always more critical than electric light. So do it by a window or, failing that, under fluorescent lighting. For evening make-up, sit in front of a centrally positioned electric light (like an angle-poise). Use a hand mirror for really close work, like applying mascara.

(2) Apply make-up on skin which is freshly cleansed, toned and moisturised. Wait about five minutes for your skin to settle before you begin.

(3) Give yourself sufficient time to do a good job. Rushed make-up never looks professional—you're too likely to make heavyhanded mistakes. Plan your look before you begin, laying out all your equipment in front of you. A really meticulous glamour make-up can take an hour or even two, but you can build up speed by experimenting and practising when your time's your own. Half an hour is realistic for a well made-up face.

(4) Always use the correct tools for the job and clean brushes and sponge after each make-up.

(5) Keep your make-up items themselves clean and tidy. For the amount of products you need as a model, an ordinary make-up bag is inadequate. Most models buy plastic tool or fishing-tackle boxes. The compartments and trays normally reserved for nuts and bolts suit make-up items perfectly.

Tools of the trade

To perfect the art of make-up, you must learn how to use the right applicator for each make-up product. Fingers may do a wonderful preliminary dotting and smoothing job, but they can't blend in tricky crevices as brushes can or phase away tidemarks and hard blusher lines with the same care as sponges and puffs. The well-equipped make-up box should contain:

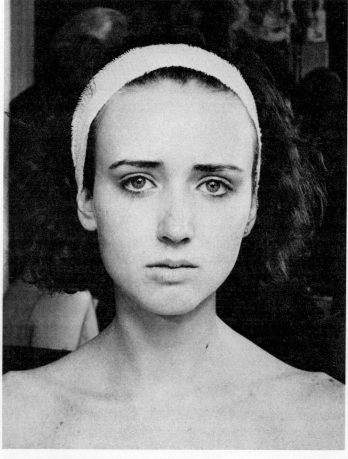

Almost any girl anxious about ordinary features . . .

(1) Cosmetic sponges for evenly applying foundation and cream blusher.

(2) Large, flat velveteen puff for gently pressing loose powder over foundation.

(3) Chunky round blusher brush for applying powder blushers.

(4) Sponge-tip applicators for applying dense areas of powder shadow.

(5) Medium-size, firm, flat brushes for blending powder and cream shadows.

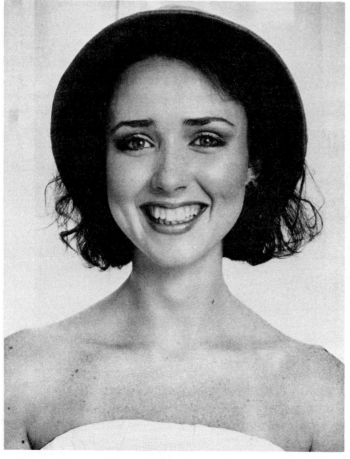

. . . can be delighted by the magic of the expert.
Make-up by Kate Smart at Lucie Clayton's

(6) Thin eyeliner brush for liquid liners.

(7) Eyebrow brush to groom brows and brush off powder.

(8) Small, narrow lip brush, square or wedge-shaped for accurate lip-painting.

(9) Cotton wool buds for general blending, removing blobs and smudges, cleaning inner eye corners.

(10) Eyelash curlers.

(11) Tweezers.

(12) Hairband or thick elastic ribbon to keep your hair off your face.

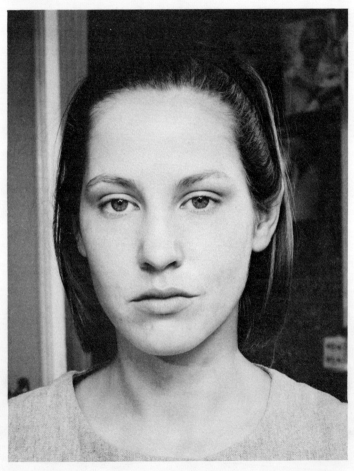

Practice alone can give you the skill to transform an average face . . .

Never buy nylon brushes, even though they're cheap. They are inflexible, prone to moult hairs and drag make-up. The very best brushes are sable for the smaller ones, like eye-shadow and lip brushes, and a mix of badger and sable for the larger brushes. All your brushes should have long handles, like painter's brushes, for maximum control. They *are* costly, so you may have to build up your collection slowly, especially as it's practical to have more than one of

. . . into a glamorous work of art. Make-up by Abigail Morcombe-White at Lucie Clayton's

each variety, keeping one set for dark shades and another for lighter tones. Good temporary stopgaps are the basic sets sold in chemists and department stores—but always test them for softness and flexibility by brushing them against the back of your hand before you buy them. You may well find some make-up palettes contain perfectly adequate applicators. Sponge-tips are especially useful: wash and save them after you've used up the product. Old brushes are like old friends—get to know them and they help you tremendously. When you have to replace them, try to match them with identical new ones, or at worst, similar models so your make-up technique is kept as consistent as possible.

Laying the foundations

The most important stage of any make-up is the foundation work. Your foundation evens out your skin tone, lifting and enhancing your natural complexion and provides a smooth, constant base for the rest of your colours to sit on. It is the closest colour cosmetic to your skin itself and it should look as natural as your skin and not contrast visibly with your neck. It makes sense to wear foundation from a protective point of view. Many foundations have built-in sunscreens and moisturisers to shield your skin from losing moisture and forming premature wrinkles. But for your foundation to look absolutely natural, stay put and provide that stable base for all the rest, you must choose the right shade and formula for your skin type.

Check your texture

The last thing you need is a heavy, greasy foundation if you've an oily skin, or a skimpy water-based fluid if you're the dry type. So a logical first move when you're hunting for your perfect product is to look in your favourite skincare range. Growing numbers of cosmetic manufacturers are extending their ranges with compatible colour cosmetics, so it's a fair bet that if their moisturisers suit you, so will their foundations. By and large, the richer and thicker the foundation, the more coverage and moisturiser it offers.

Test the product on your face itself if possible, or failing that, on a part of your hand or arm nearest in tone to your face. (The back of your hand is usually darker and the inside wrist lighter, so beware!) Take your 'patch test' into the daylight (electric light often distorts colour) and wait at least an hour before you finally decide.

Check the texture—if it looks greasy, then it's too rich for your skin type; if it disappears, then you need a richer formula.

Applying foundation

Begin your make-up on a cool skin, ten minutes after you've moisturised.

(1) Shake the foundation to make sure the ingredients are evenly blended. Dot a little over forehead, nose, cheeks and chin.

(2) Dampen your cosmetic sponge with cool water, then squeeze dry in a towel. Sweep the foundation lightly up and out to your hairline, over your forehead, and across your cheeks. Then sweep up and out over your chin, sponging a little way under your jawbone. Sponge over the area between your lip and nose, then pinching your sponge to a point, work around the nostrils and inner eye corners. Looking up, gently dab under your eyes then, closing lids, sweep across and outwards towards temples. With the clean side of the sponge, brush upwards against the downy hairs along your top lip and the sides of your cheeks and hairline, to unclog and blend out tidemarks. Stroke upwards from just under your chin onto your jawline to phase in the foundation tone. There is no need to make up your neck for normal daywear, unless you feel it is excessively pale or mottled. Even then, the scantest foundation is sufficient—try sweeping over with the remainder of colour on your sponge.

(3) Double check your blending with your clean fingertips, being extra careful around eyes and nostrils. Top make-up

artist Barbara Daly believes finger work is essential. Not only are fingers extremely good at blending, but touching your face means you get to know it intimately and learn more about its structure than a mirror can tell you.

Hiding the blemishes

Faint shadows may simply need an extra dabbing of foundation to hush them. But spots, blotches and deeper discoloration need heavier duty concealers. These are, in fact, concentrated foundations and there are several kinds on the market, varying slightly in texture. The most effective are the solid sticks or pots of concealer which are firm textured, neither too dry nor greasy to blend. Easy to use also are the 'automatic' concealers, slightly more fluid and found in tubes with their own sponge-tip applicators.

Your concealer should be one or two shades lighter than your foundation to cancel out effectively areas which are darker than the rest of your face. But the art of clever concealing is to cover imperceptibly. There should be no give-away white stripes and dots if your blending has been 100 per cent meticulous!

Applying your concealer

(1) Work a little concealer onto a clean, firm flat brush and paint a strip under each eye, where the shadow is deepest. If your eyes are deepset, paint concealer in the inner eye corners.

(2) Ease laughter lines and creases round the mouth and frown lines between the brows by tracing concealer along them. Brush several strokes across cheeks to cancel out veins and high colour.

(3) With the brush, dab concealer over spots and blotches.

(4) Wait a couple of minutes for the concealer to become very slightly 'tacky', so that it adheres well to the foundation. Lightly dab-press the concealer, blending it into the foundation without rubbing or dragging it off. If the blemish still shows through, press on a touch more concealer until it

vanishes. If the concealer shows too obviously pale, p
a light film of foundation. If your finger seems to be wip
off the concealer rather than blending it in, blend instead
with feather-light brush strokes.

The perfect powder

Powder is to foundation what varnish is to an oil-painting. It
seals, sets and fixes, whilst it helps even out the tone. It also
absorbs shine and grease which seeps through the foundation
during the day. It is important to apply your foundation
before you use powder products like blushers and eyeshadows, in order to provide a dry base for them to glide
evenly over. But use cream blushers and shadows directly
over foundation, and powder *afterwards* to set.

The very best powders are the ultra-fine loose ones found
in tubs or boxes. These translucent types are unlikely to
look dull or floury if dusted on lightly. Compact or block
powders are obviously denser in texture and are useful for
carrying around for re-touches during the day or for applying directly onto moisturised skin to take off the shine
and even your skin tone, if you can't be bothered with
foundation.

Try to buy a completely transparent or colourless powder
so that it cannot deepen your foundation tone. Failing that,
opt for a shade lighter than your foundation. As with
pearly foundations, avoid using too much of the pearlised
types as they really can make your skin look greasy. Use
them for highlighting only. (See the section on page 124 on
face-shaping.)

Applying powder

(1) Dip a large, flat puff into the loose powder, then tap
off the excess on the back of your hand.

(2) Hold the puff at the base, then slap-pat the powder
over your face and press it firmly into the foundation.

(3) Dust off any excess with cotton wool.

g your face is achieved by clever placing , to highlight your best features and play ..ems. You can give the illusion of a smaller ..eekbones, a shorter chin or a more definite jaw......earning to use your contour kit with skill and subtle..

You need three basic depths of tone to 'sculpt' your face. The deepest is the **shader**. This can be a dark face powder or foundation one or two tones darker than your skintone, or a purpose-made tawny face-shaper or blusher. Its job is to create shadows, to slim, minimise and hollow, so it should be essentially matt. Any sheen would catch the light and bring it to the fore.

The **blusher** is mid-tone, which brings colour and warmth to your face and livens your skin. Depending on where it is applied, it can also back up the work of the shader, gently blending in and making a subtle grading of tone. It is the only member of your contour kit which should be at all obvious, and it should tone with your lip colour for the most natural effect.

The **highlighter** does just that. It's job is to pick out your 'high spots' like cheekbones, browbones, chin and centre of your nose if you need to. Invariably it is pearlised to catch the maximum light and can be peach, ivory or white with a silver or gold sheen. Like blushers, it may be a cream or loose or compressed powder. For more subtle highlighting, you can also use a very light face powder or baby talc.

Some manufacturers make it easy for you by making 'shape and shade' palettes with all three ingredients at the ready. But it's generally best to collect your own separate products to tally with your skin tone.

Applying shader and highlighter

Light and shade work closely together, the one strengthening the work of the other. If you are using cream products, remember to apply them directly onto the foundation and powder them afterwards. Begin by stippling on a very small amount first with your fingertips, gradually building up as you need to. Dabbing with a cosmetic sponge is an easy, light way to apply a cream shader, blending it into the foundation with your fingertips so there are no hard lines or edges. Powder products are the easiest to apply and control, as you can gauge the build-up of colour with the lightest flick of the brush. Using them *after* you have powdered your foundation means the intensity of light and shade is unaffected by powdering later. You can also use your powder puff to blend out edges and temper your shades if you need to.

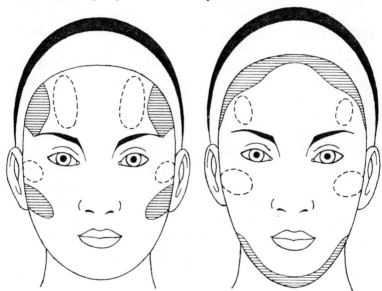

Slimming a plump face   Shortening a long face

Slimming a plump face

Shade the temple hollows just in front of the hairline and create more definite hollows under the cheekbones. (Sucking in your cheeks helps you see where the shading should be.) Apply highlighter on the browbones, blending up beyond the brow itself to bring the bone forward. Highlight the cheekbone from its highest point along towards the hairline.

Shortening a long face

Blend shader from just under the chin, slightly upwards onto the chin mound. Shade the forehead at the temples, working round next to the hairline, gradually fading out at mid brow. Lightly shade around the jawline. Highlight the cheekbones and browbones.

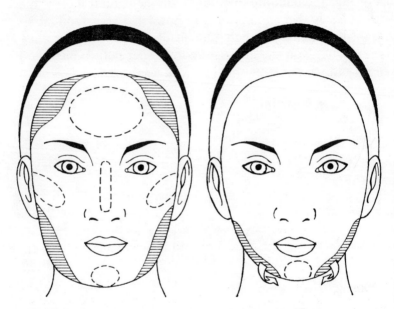

Softening a square face   Strengthening a weak chin

Softening a square face

Shade the four corner 'angles' of the face: the temples, following the hairline round just onto the brow; the 'squares' of the jawbones from below the ears to either side of the chin. Highlight the lower half of the chin, the centre brow, down the nose and the cheekbones.

Strengthening a weak chin

Lightly shade just underneath the jawbone along the jawline itself. Highlight the chin.

Softening a pointed chin

Blend the shader upwards onto the chin. Highlight the jaw-bone either side of the chin.

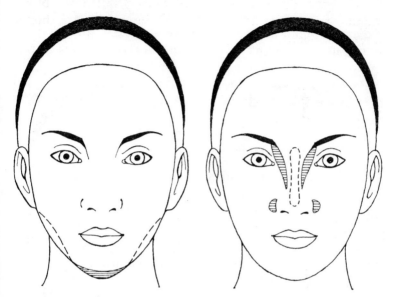

Softening a pointed chin   Slimming a wide nose

Slimming a wide nose

Blend the shader either side of the bridge, deep into the inner eye corners and faintly either side of the nose itself. Slim the nostrils by shading into the creases. Highlight all along the centre of the nose.

Applying blusher

Not only does your blusher strengthen your face shapers, but it also acts as a 'mood' cosmetic, depending on its shade and the shape in which it is applied. Strong, deep blushers, for example, can look sophisticated for evenings, whilst rose-pink and coral blushers look fresh and glowing for a natural day-time look. Vibrant colours are a strong fashion idea for parties.

Your colour choice is largely determined by your skin tone, plus your choice of clothes. Pale skins can take most shades well, but soft coral and warm rose tints flatter them, counter-acting bluish tints in fine skin. Olive skins suit warm pinks which lift sallow tones. Tawny and black skins suit intense reds, rusts and oranges which make use of their own, natural yellow tones. Intense blue-reds and fuschias also look attrac-tive on coloured skins, especially for evenings.

Powders are always the easiest textures to use as you can control them with a flick of the brush.

A healthy outdoors look

Choose a warm tone, either coral, rust or tawny-rose. Be-ginning on the 'apple' of the cheeks (where the bone is at its roundest) blend along the cheekbone itself angling upwards and fading out onto the temples. Blend on the browbones, up and out to the sides, through the outer eyebrow and fading into the hairline on the temples. Check the edges with a powder puff. Touch a little blusher on the lower part of the chin.

A sophisticated evening look

Choose a blue-red or plum toned blusher. Beginning slightly to the side of the 'apple', angle the blusher just underneath the cheekbone, fading out towards the hairline. The shape should be that of a triangle turned on its side. (But the edges, of course, should be blended to extinction!)

A high-fashion party look

Choose an intense fuchsia or orange-toned blusher. Blend high on the cheekbones, beginning just below the outer eye corners, working towards the hairline. Keeping the colour to the outer parts of the face, blend up onto the temples and outer browbones, taking the colour right up, fading into the hairline at either side of the forehead.

Making the most of your eyes

There is so much more to eye make-up than simply colouring your lids. Your eyes are even more expressive than your lips. They have the power of implying emotion without the rest of your face even twitching a muscle. (Something all models learn very quickly!) It's hardly surprising, then, that cosmetic counters groan under a battery of the various types of eye products and our make-up bags bulge with more items for your eyes than for any other part of our face. Eye make-up is a jungle of colours which need decoding before we let it anywhere near our eyes.

Eye shadows

Eye shadows are obviously the most prominent members of anyone's eye kit. They can be pearly or matt, in compressed or loose powder form, firm creams in pots or sticks, or thinner fluids, usually with their own sponge-tip applicators. Thankfully, most of the creams are crease- and melt-proof, but a scant pressing of translucent powder is still an insurance if the weather is hot or your lids have deep creases. It used to be the rule that your choice of colour was dictated by your own eye shade. Nowadays, we're much more flexible, matching our eyes to our clothes.

Some shades, though, flatter more than others. **Browns** are gentle enough to suit all eye colours, intensifying pale eyes by sheer contrast and making brown eyes look richer. **Blues** are less amenable. They can look cold or wishy-washy if they are too pale, hard if they are too dark, and do absolutely nothing at all for coloured skins. But they do a wonderful job of brightening bloodshot eyewhites and cooling puffy lids and red rims (you've got a cold, say, or you've been crying) and can also be used to highlight other shades. **Mauves**, **pinks** and **lavenders** are best used with other toning shades (look for the colour co-ordinated palettes). **Greens** can look stark if they are too intense or too pale, but **olive** tones can be marvellously flattering, giving a very natural warmth for an outdoors look. Usually, it's best to use a low-key pearl or

...ow for daytime, although a little pearl highlighter
...s and makes all the difference at any time.

Eye pencils

Eye pencils fall into four groups. The chunky, often pearly
crayons serve the same purpose as cream shadows. Their
great advantage is the ease with which you can control their
colour. This makes them particularly good for eye shaping.

Kohl or **kajal pencils** are often slimline and used for soft,
smudgy lining around the eyes and along the inner rim. Their
much less stable textures sometimes causes them to smudge a
little too much. But a light primer of neutral or coloured
powder shadow around the lids first, helps hold them in
check.

Liner pencils serve the same function as kohl, and look
similar in their slimline form. Generally, they are quite hard
(and tend to go harder in cold weather, needing a few seconds
of working on the back of your hand to make them soft
enough to trace gently around your eyes).

Eyebrow pencils are thin, matt and come in a variety of
browns. It's often a good idea to use more than one shade
for textured, natural-looking brow work. Accurate results
also need sharp pencil points. To help prevent the 'lead'
crumbling in the sharpener, leave the pencil overnight to
harden in the fridge.

Eye liners

In addition to liner pencils, there is also a choice of formulae
for brush application.

Liquid liners often come in little bottles with their own
liner brushes attached to the cap. Always check your strokes
on the back of your hand before you commit brush to lid—
the liner may need thinning, to avoid blobs and blotches,
although with some waterproof liners, this may not be possible.

Cake liners are the original classics. You mix up your own
consistency with water, depending on how strong you want

your colour to be. In fact, it should be possible to experiment with powder shadows in the same way. Mix with a little water for a liner which cleverly complements the basic shadow colour.

A basic eye make-up technique

(1) **The base.** Lightly coat the lids with foundation to provide a smooth base for cream and powder-shadows alike.

(2) **The shadow.** Apply cream shadows directly onto the foundation. With your fingertip, smudge a circle of shadow over the centre lids. Then with a firm, flat brush, blend all over the lids, working well into the sockets and fading half-way up onto the browbone. Add a touch more cream if you need to strengthen the colour.

An alternative method is to powder your lids before using a powder shadow. Work a little of the shadow onto a sponge applicator, then trace along the socket line from deep in the inner eye corners, over and out to the outer lid edge. With the tip of the sponge, trace a smudge-line of shadow next to the lower lashes. Should you find that applicator sponges are a little 'heavy handed', try blending with a flat shadow brush. Powder shadow can also be applied with a slightly damp brush for greater depth of tone, or greater control over very dark shades which tend to 'sprinkle' downwards onto your cheeks.

(3) **The highlighter.** Cream highlighters of course go straight over cream shadows or pencils. Powder highlighters are for powder shadows only. Choose your highlighter to complement your shadow colour. Gold and silver are good all-rounders for evening and emphasise the sheen in most pearlised shadows. Two-tone lights give an added dimension to strong make-up. Warmer sheeny pinks, peaches and gold-ivories lend subtle lights to day make-up. It's easier to concentrate the strength of your highlight with a sponge applicator, as brushes, although the best tools for blending, do tend to diffuse colour. Highlight your lids at the very centre by applying a round spot, then brushing slightly to the sides to graduate the sheen gently. Highlight the browbone just

under the brow's highest arch (usually just off-centre, towards the temples).

(4) **The liner.** Lining all around the eyes is thankfully out of fashion. It is the most difficult thing of all to trace steadily accurate, subtly tapering lines without making them look thick and hard. These days it seems sufficient to pencil along the outer lids only, or simply underline the eyes next to the lashes along the lower lids. Smudge to a more natural haze with a cotton wool bud.

(5) **Eyelash curlers.** These are often left out, regarded as optional extras. But for a really professional eye make-up, lash curlers make all the difference, curling and separating lashes, making them look longer, and your eyes more open. Lash curlers themselves look like instruments of pure torture—like scissors with curved blades and rubber buffers instead of cutting edges. But once you're used to them, eyelash curlers are surprisingly simple to manipulate. Gently open them wide and position them over your lashes, the curve corresponding to the curve of your half-opened lids. Slowly close the curlers, making sure that the rubber edges fit snugly over the lashes, just clear of the lid rims. Squeeze and hold the curlers closed for ten seconds, then release them. Your lashes should now be curled. Some people prefer to use the lash curlers after mascara, as they say they 'set' the lashes better. But if you're inexperienced, you can all too easily squeeze the lashes together—and they do become very difficult to separate!

(6) **Mascara.** Most of the blobs and smudges are made by jabbing at the lashes with an overloaded brush. Firm, slow sweeps are the key to well-coated lashes and unscathed surrounding lids. Make sure your brush is evenly coated with mascara, with no gluts or clogs. Look down into your mirror and firmly brush the top side of your upper lashes. Still looking downwards, slowly close your lashes several times onto the brush, so that the undersides of the lashes are evenly coated. Separate clogged lashes with a clean, dry mascara brush. Wait a minute before looking upwards, to avoid hitting your browbone with the tips of your wet lashes. Looking upwards into the mirror, coat your lower lashes with the tip

of the mascara wand, stroking across them
inwards. Straighten them with the flat of the
lightly downwards. Repeat the whole proces
more dramatic emphasis to your lashes.

Brow shaping

Eyebrows frame the eyes and give expression to the whole of
the face. There is no such thing as the perfect thickness,
though. How strong your brows are should relate directly to
the strength of your features. Delicate bone-structures are
overshadowed by heavy, bushy brows, whereas stronger
features may need substantial brows to balance them.

Brows also change with fashion. At the end of the Sixties
brows were plucked to a fine, 1920s style arch, giving everyone a moon-eyed, wistful look of surprise. Towards the end
of the Seventies, bushiness came back into fashion with the
Margaux Hemingway era of brows brushed and slicked
upwards with gel! Nowadays, we're somewhere in between
with well-groomed brows, substantial enough to complement
the eyes without dominating the face.

There is such a thing, though, as the perfect *shape*. Your
brows should begin at their thickest, directly above the inner
eye corners, tapering to the highest point of their arch, above
the outer edge of the iris. Lay a pencil from the corner of the
nostrils past the outer eye corner. Where the natural curve of
the brow meets the pencil on the browbone, there your brow
should finely taper to its end.

Keep the brows well-trimmed by tweezing out the stray
hairs below and above the main body of the brow, so that
make-up cannot clog around them and create shadows or
smudges. Choose a springy, preferably wedge-shaped pair
of tweezers for a firm grip, and check daily for stragglers
in a good light. It goes without saying that you should do
your tweezing before you begin your make-up. If you find
plucking very painful, a compress with a warm face flannel
will help open your pores and loosen the hairs. Your regular toner and moisturiser will soothe your skin afterwards.

Always groom your brows with a damp eyebrow brush

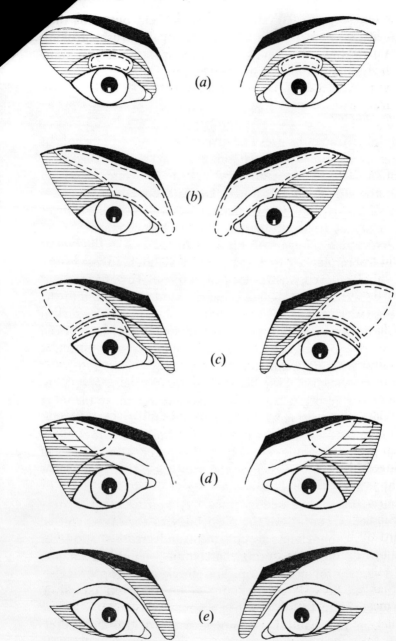

Corrections for: (*a*) Deepset eyes; (*b*) Close-together eyes; (*c*) Wide-apart eyes;
(*d*) Sloping eyes; (*e*) Slanting eyes

after make-up, to free them of foundation and powder. If your brows are sparse, or too fair, echo nature with an eyebrow pencil sharpened to a gimlet point. Draw quick, light hairfine strokes, following the direction of your natural hair growth. A blend of two shades of pencil gives the most natural, textured effect.

Eye shaping

You can correct eye shapes with the same selective use of light and shade which you relied on to shape your face. Here are some basic correction techniques. Drawings page 134.

Deep-set eyes. Eyes with a greater proportion of browbone to lid need evening out with mid-toned shadow, blended over the lids themselves, then upwards three-quarters of the way over the browbone. Highlight the centre of the lids right next to the lashes, but not the browbone.

Close-together eyes. Draw them wider apart by concentrating a deep-toned shadow on the outer halves of the lids, blending outwards past the outer corners and fading up onto the browbones towards the temples. Widen the space at the inner corners by applying a light shadow.

Wide-apart eyes. Draw them closer together by reversing the technique for close-set eyes. Blend the darker shadow deep into the inner corners and onto the sides of the nose bridge, then lighten the outer lids. Apply a fairly strong highlight just under the brows, on a line with the inner edge of the iris.

Sloping eyes. Counteract that rather sad-looking downward tilt by sweeping colour up and over the outer lids onto the browbone and highlighting the bone itself fairly strongly, slightly outwards from the centre.

Slanting eyes. Cat's eyes can be extremely attractive, so by all means, go with them! But when you don't want to feel so feline, weight them at the outer corners by blending a deep liner from the mid-point of the lower lids, thickening towards the outer eye corners. Take a very fine line only slightly in from the outer corners on the upper lids. A mid to deep-toned shadow, blended into the inner corners, balances out the shape.

Painting your lips

Lipstick is so much more than just the finishing touch. The colour of your lips has an enormous effect on the rest of your face, pulling all your make-up into focus, heightening, dulling or enhancing its effect. For this reason, you may well find yourself double-checking your cheek and eye colours after you've painted on your lips. The blusher that seemed just that little bit 'over the top' when it overshadowed your pale, bare mouth, could suddenly sink back into place against a full-bodied lipstick. Eyes that seemed dark and heavy could come to life with a rich lip colour to help them. Conversely, pale lip shades leave all the emphasis to eyes (a fashion exploited to the full in the infamous Sixties), especially if the blusher is 'laid-back' too.

On a practical note, wearing lipstick keeps your lips moist and prevents flaking and chapping, especially in the very hot or cold weather. So wearing some form of lip product is good therapy.

Lip liner pencils have the same fine point as do eye liner pencils and are required to do the same precision work. They are quite hard and dry in comparison to lipstick itself as their function is not only to provide an accurate outline to contain the lip colour, but to help prevent the lip colour 'bleeding' off past the lip edges. Chunky **lip crayons**, however, are much softer and are similar in texture to lipsticks. Although their crayon 'point' makes them reasonably accurate without using a brush, they are only marginally more stable than lipsticks themselves, if at all.

All lip colour, in whatever form, comes in both **plain** (sometimes called cream) or **pearlised** (sometimes called frosted) formulae. Generally speaking, the pearl agent acts as a stabiliser, slightly drying and stiffening the texture, giving a longer-lasting finish. Cream colours on the whole tend to look warmer, richer and are best for daytime. Silver pearls can look brash or cold, depending on the colour and the rest of the make-up and are best left to evenings. Gold glints are flattering for evening, and used sparingly, liven daytime lips.

Choice of colour

How should you choose your lip colour? Like your cheeks, your lips should flatter and liven your complexion. Very **dark** skins look exotic with bright 'punchy' flames and fuchsias. **Sallow** complexions should avoid yellow tones, like oranges and some browns. **Pale** skins should be wary that strong, vivid colours don't harden the look, or leap out starkly from the face.

But perhaps the most important factor influencing your colour choice is your outfit. Your lipstick must always tone, if not match your clothes, or if you're wearing dark shades like black, navy and brown, or neutrals like oatmeal, grey and white, it should contrast tastefully, preferably matching your accessories. A chic, stylised example of colour co-ordination is a black suit and white blouse, with red lips and nails to match a smart pair of red clip-on earrings. Plain, but stunningly effective.

Applying your lip colour

(1) Lipsticks 'sit' best on a smooth dry base. Prepare your lips with a scant film of foundation set with a dusting of powder.

(2) With a liner pencil chosen to tone with, but slightly darker than your final colour, outline your lips, keeping to the very edge of your natural contour. Begin by defining the 'V' of your cupid's bow, then extend the line either side down to the mouth corners. Follow the lip line down either side of the lower lip, meeting at the centre. There is no need to pull your mouth into a tight-lipped grin. You can see exactly how you are working on relaxed lips, very slightly apart.

(3) Work a little lip colour onto a lip brush. Begin filling in the outline by firmly and carefully brushing upwards from the mouth corners towards the cupid's bow on either side of

the upper lip, then down and up under the cupid's bow. Travel downwards towards the centre on either side of the lower lip brushing across at the centre with short, controlled strokes. Do not overload the brush at first, and do not cross the lip line. Although brushes give you maximum accuracy for the camera, if your hand is steady and well-practised, you can fill in your lip line straight from the stick, so long as you keep well inside the lip contour.

(4) Build up the colour if necessary with a second layer. If you want a richer, more shiny effect, brush a clear or frosted gloss over the centre of the lips only where it can't run off at the edges.

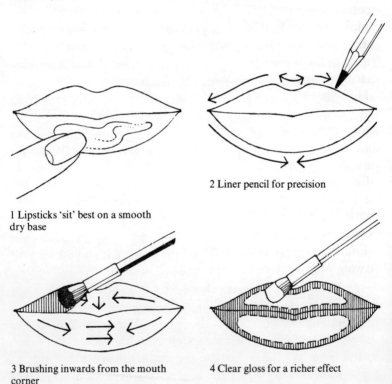

1 Lipsticks 'sit' best on a smooth dry base

2 Liner pencil for precision

3 Brushing inwards from the mouth corner

4 Clear gloss for a richer effect

Reshaping your mouth

As well as defining your lips, a lip liner can also correct and improve their shape. Slim down full lips by colouring inside the natural contour (a foundation base is doubly vital here!) and fill out skimpy lips by taking the line just outside. Similarly, you can build up or take away lop-sided or poorly defined contours, creating an even, well-proportioned mouth. Corrective work always calls for firm-textured lipsticks that won't smudge, bleed or give the game away.

Highlighting your lips

Edging your lips with sheeny highlighter powder gives them party 'punch' and defines flatter lips, plumping them out that bit more. Choose a soft silver, gold or peachy tone and, with a cotton wool bud, trace over the lip edges emphasising the cupid's bow and upper lip before you use your liner pencil. The powder also stops the lip colour bleeding. Paint just a touch on the centre of the lips too, to highlight and stabilise, or to give a non-pearl colour a sheeny finish.

How to get a really much more sophisticated effect without that glossy overtone: paint on a fairly generous coating of colour then blot with a tissue, holding it firm and taut over your lips with both hands, being extra careful not to smudge the edges. Repeat until the pigment in the lipstick has adhered sufficiently evenly to the foundation underneath and most of the grease has been absorbed by the tissue. Double check and strengthen your lip edges by going over them without recharging your lip brush.

For the professional technique of applying make-up for catwalk and camera, see Appendix 2 at the end of the book.

12
The Model Walk

Deportment may sound an anachronism—a ritual from the past, carried out by schoolgirls in gym-slips with dictionaries on their heads, or a practice confined to the world of débutantes, 'coming out' with poise, gliding serenely in their ballgowns as if time were never at their heels. Either way, it's a stuffy word that reeks of old-fashioned values. Or is it?

Most people don't realise how atrociously they do walk. Time after time, the girls who come to my courses are aghast when they see videos of themselves as they really are on the first day. Then at the end of their training, they tell me how learning the model walk has made them not only more aware of themselves, but they notice how badly everyone else walks out there in the street!

Future model or no, everyone should learn how to walk properly. If you just stand tall, instantly you look better, your clothes fit better and hang properly. You look slimmer, better proportioned and you feel much more relaxed and comfy—even in the bus or supermarket queue! For a model, posture is doubly vital. Not only does she need the grace and body control to perform that epic of precision we call cat-walking, but she needs to make the clothes she wears look so good that everyone will want them. If she's slouching along, chin on chest, shoulders hunched and feet plodding like a penguin's, neither she nor the clothes will look anything more than limp. With her head up and smiling and a spring in her step, she should radiate the confidence that will make her clothes *live*.

By and large, lack of confidence is the culprit behind bad deportment. Analysing a new pupil from the head downwards, I find that very few actually stand or sit with their head line conforming with their shoulders; the head is either tilted to one side or the chin is flopping down on the chest, eyes trained on the feet. They never look forward, those eyes. The angle of the head means they're avoiding *your* eyes; it's impossible to look straight at you from that position! Then we see what happens to the shoulders. A tilted head means one shoulder is dipped. Years of satchel-carrying also take their toll; you can even tell whether a person is right- or left-handed by the way the body tilts.

A dropped chin means hunched shoulders, which inevitably means a droopy bust, a spare tyre and a flabby tummy. You can visually lose pounds by straightening up. But a low shoulder means that one hip is dropped and it's this imbalance that causes a jerky or bouncy walk. You either look as though you've a slight limp, or you wriggle your hips awkwardly as you drop your weight from side to side, or gyrate your pelvis from front to back. Then your knees bend too far when you walk and if you're not careful, you look as if you're walking on springs—everything bounces from your head downwards.

Feet are another problem. Eight out of ten girls are pigeon-toed—they plod with their feet turning inwards so that their weight falls forward, everything droops and they look as if they could get a train between their ankles.

The opposite problem occurs when a girl is knock-kneed. Her thighs look as if they're glued together and her feet splay outwards. Girls who are overweight tend to walk like this; it makes them look fatter than they actually are, because of the way they *waddle*. If they learned to cross their feet slightly in front of one another, they would look so much slimmer. It's an old model-girl trick—never face the camera with your body full on.

But there lies another danger. Cross your feet over too far and your hips swing round. So you're back to the case of the gyrating pelvis.

Finally, your taste in shoes may not be helping you. If you chose the wrong shape for your feet, you'll have trouble keeping them on and this will affect the way you walk. Shoes

...des are the worst—especially for high insteps
feet. Making sure your shoes give your feet
,pport pays off, not only from the comfort angle
,ough your deportment, for appearance's sake.

Learning to walk again

Having established your faults, some of which may have
come as quite a shock, you may well have a daunting task in
correcting them. Admittedly, it is also a painstaking one. Just
as you can't learn to run before you can walk, with the model
walk the correction begins with your basic standing position.
It could take you days of practice before you find your balance; then comes the footwork. It will seem extremely odd at
first—even unnatural. Perfectly placed, dainty steps will not
come easily to an ex-tomboy who has spent her life charging
after energetic brothers. At the very least, it will cramp your
style—your *old* style that is. But once you've practised and
mastered the fairly dogmatic walk and complex turns, you
gradually build up speed and add that bit of your own
character and flair that will culminate in a relaxed, confident
walk.

On the ramp, or catwalk, most models translate it into a
dance. It looks effortless, fluid, in perfect time to the music.
It may even be a specially choreographed 'dance-walk',
especially when a large collection is being shown and several
models are working together. But watch their feet. The basic
steps are never far away. They know that those steps mean
balance and control. But from that departure, the possibilities
are endless. After all, as we've discovered before in this book,
rules are made to be broken.

Step one: standing

(1) Stand very tall, feet together, toes turning slightly outwards, stretching up with your head as if you're a puppet,
pulled by the strings. Your whole body is being lifted towards
the ceiling.

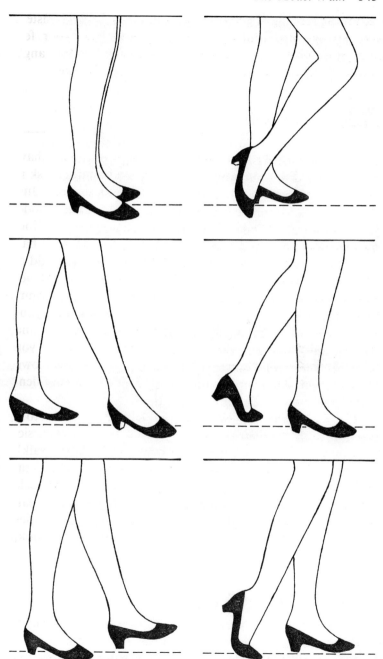

Learning the model walk (pages 142–5) will make any girl look better, feel better

(2) Relax your head back into your shoulders, so that it sits squarely, facing the front.

(3) Put your hands on your hips to help you balance and feel your body's alignment. Pull your head up out of your shoulders again and push your shoulders back and relax them. Do *not* stick your chest out or clench your elbows into your sides.

(4) Lean slightly back, tucking your bottom under and pushing your pelvis forward, so that you are standing at a slight angle with your weight behind you. Practise standing like this until you feel completely at ease with your balance. This basic philosophy of keeping your weight always behind you is one golden rule of balance which applies to all the movements in the model walk.

(5) Relax your arms at your sides and take your weight onto your left leg, keeping your knee straight. Bend your right knee and, keeping your right foot arched and tucked into your left ankle, practise standing like a stork. If your body deviates from its slight angle backwards, you *will* wobble and fall over. But if your back is slightly arched, your head up, your buttocks tucked under and your pelvis forward you should maintain the control to stay standing comfortably on one leg for quite a time.

(6) Change the weight to your right leg and practise standing with your left foot raised.

Step two: the walk

(1) Using your basic stance as a starting point, both feet on the floor, turning slightly outwards and legs straight, with your hands on your hips for balance, take the weight on your left leg.

(2) All model walk movements begin with the right foot. Arch your right foot and raise it up off the floor, keeping your ankles together.

(3) Bring your right foot forward and around in front of your left so that your right heel is on a line with your left heel. Place your foot down starting with the heel, then the instep and finally the ball of the foot, toe out. (You should

be able to feel the muscles stretch along your shinbone.) The distance between your front heel and your back toe should be half the length of your foot. So in fact your stride is one and a half times your foot. Your heels should always be in line—as if you're walking a tightrope with the toes pointing slightly outwards.

(4) Both legs should now be straight. To transfer the weight from your left (back) to your right (front) foot, bend the left leg and at the same time, turn the left toe outwards whilst raising the heel off the ground, then the toe, arching the ankle.

(5) Bring the left foot through, barely clipping ankles and stretching the muscles down the shinbone as you arch the instep, keeping the toes turned outwards. Imagine your foot is a paintbrush, sweeping through, painting a line with your heel. Bring your heel round in front of your right toe, place it down again, then the instep and the ball of your foot until both legs are straight again. The only time your leg is bent is when you're lifting a foot to take a step. Both legs are never bent at the same time.

(6) Take another step with your right foot, transferring the weight to your left leg—and so on, toes turned out, ankles together as they pass, heel and toe on a line and never further apart than half the length of one foot, weight always on the back leg.

The three turns

Successful turns are a combination of balance and surefootedness. 'Turning on a sixpence' gives an idea of the precision and neatness with which they should be performed; so practice (and your fair share of toppling over at first!) is essential if you're to perfect these precarious movements. Again, go through them slowly to begin with, establishing your footwork. Then build up speed, flair and flourish.

The three turns used in modelling are the **basic**, the **full** and the **Paris** turn. Most girls find the basic turn the most difficult to get the hang of and it's probably the one they'll

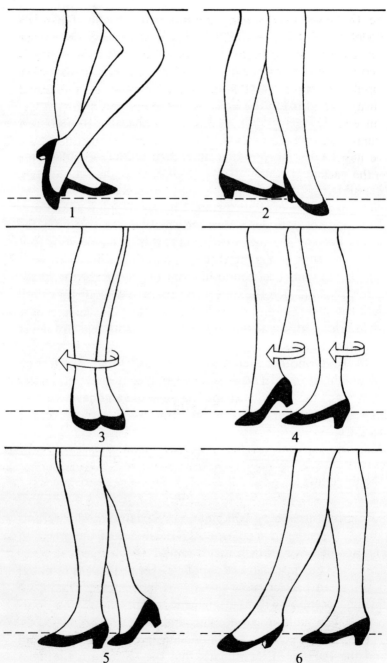

Basic turn. After 2, bring left foot parallel with right into position 3. See pages 148–9

use the least as it's generally associated with showroom modelling. But it does teach you to control and pivot your feet, as well as forming the basis of the full turn which is used all the time on the catwalk. The Paris turn is the other popular catwalk 'twirl' and is the simplest of the three. Always, you turn to the right. With the basic and Paris turns, you end up facing in the opposite direction; the full turn brings you right round, back to the start. During the turns, the usual rules of model walking still apply—weight always to the back, tail tucked under, chin up and relax, if you can.

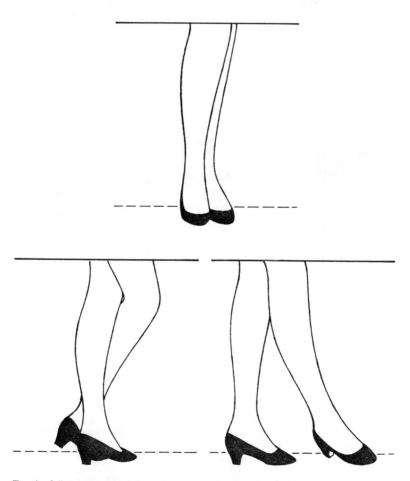

For the full turn see page 149

The basic turn

(1) Begin with your basic standing position; weight on your straight, left leg, right leg slightly bent with the heel of the right foot raised, tucked neatly into the left ankle.

(2) With your weight still on your left leg, step forward with your right foot, angling towards the right, so that the heel of your right foot is on the level line with the toes of your left. At the same time, angle your left foot, pivoting on

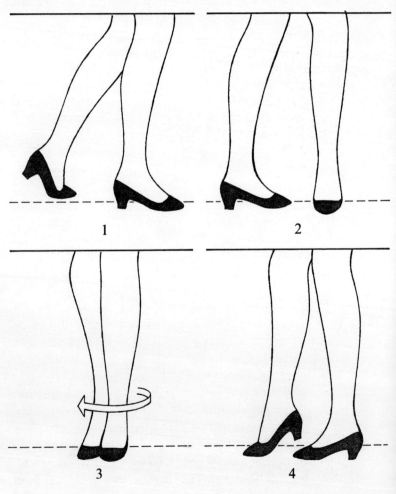

The famous Paris turn

the toes, so that both feet are parallel pointing towards the right.

(3) With the weight still on your left and your right heel off the ground, balance on the ball of your right foot and bring the left round alongside it.

(4) Swivel both feet right round, pushing out with the ball of your right foot, heel up, keeping the left on the ground.

(5) Stop for a second. Then lift up your right foot and tuck it behind the left in the third position of the feet.

(6) When you're ready, transfer the weight to your right foot (which is now at the back) and lead off with the left.

The full turn

(1) As the full turn is a continuation of the basic turn, begin with steps 1, 2 and 3 of the basic turn so that your feet are now parallel, together and angling towards the right.

(2) Balancing on the ball of your right foot, pivot both feet around as far as they will go, until they cross over and you're literally balancing on your right toenail. (This will be about three quarters round the full circle.)

(3) Let your left heel slide round slightly for balance, then instead of tucking it behind, lead off with your right foot, It's vital to keep your weight on your left leg throughout your 'twirl' otherwise you *will* lose your balance!

The Paris turn

(1) From your basic standing position, step out a little further than your normal stride with your right foot and take your weight onto it.

(2) Instead of bringing your left foot parallel, bring it around to cross in front of the right foot T-wise and immediately take your weight onto it. The distance between the two feet should be half the length of one foot.

(3) Keeping your left foot flat on the floor, raise the right heel, push out on the ball of the right foot and pivot round.

(4) With the left foot still flat, behind the right and your weight still on it, lead off with the right foot.

Showing off clothes

As we've already stressed, a fashion model's main function is to make the clothes she's wearing look so good, other people will want them. She's the prop that creates the right atmosphere, showing them off to their best possible advantage. So the idea is to make them look easy and comfortable to wear, as well as desirable. Thus you will want to bring out features like hidden pockets, a well-designed lapel, a full, swinging skirt or a dashing flash of lining.

The most difficult manoeuvre of show modelling is taking the clothes off—and putting them on again—whilst on the hoof! The catwalk does not allow for the fumbling of nervous fingers as they grab at elusive buttons, or the desperate flailing of arms, struggling free from a jacket which seems lined with sticky tape. You've enough to contend with synchronising your Paris turns with your partners, without a life or death vendetta with the Spring Collection.

To make life so much smoother, the model's mobile 'strip system' was invented. Not only is it foolproof on the catwalk, but it cuts out clumsiness and embarrassment in restaurants when the coatman's obsequious hovering seems more intent on flustering than assisting you. So practise your 'Houdini' acts at home. . . .

Coping with coats

To put on a coat of average weight (like a raincoat or a jacket), hold the collar directly above the right sleeve with your left hand, then slip your right arm into your right sleeve. Pull the collar right onto your shoulder and up to the neck. Your left coat-arm will fall parallel at the back, making it easy to find and slip into.

Button the coat from the top downwards, so you're less likely to misalign the button holes. But when you take it off again, undo your coat from the bottom upwards, using your left hand, sliding your thumb up underneath the panel to check every last button is free. Then with both hands, take the coat by the collar just above either lapel and slip it slightly back off your shoulders. Take your right hand behind your back and pull off the left sleeve by the cuff. Bring it around the front again, then take the cuff with your left hand. Also with your left hand, grip the right cuff and ease your right arm free.

You should now be holding both right and left cuffs in your left hand. (It's vital you don't drop a sleeve—the chances are you won't be able to pick it up.) Find the middle of the collar with your right hand, drop the sleeves from your left

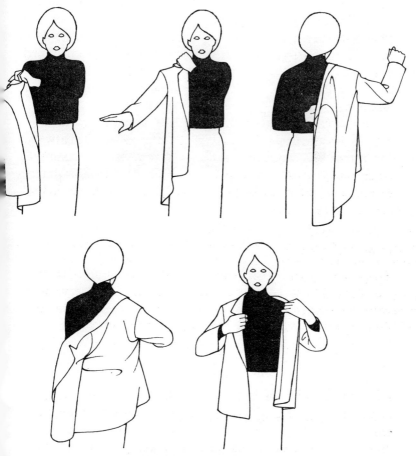

Elegant coat technique avoids a clumsy struggle on the catwalk

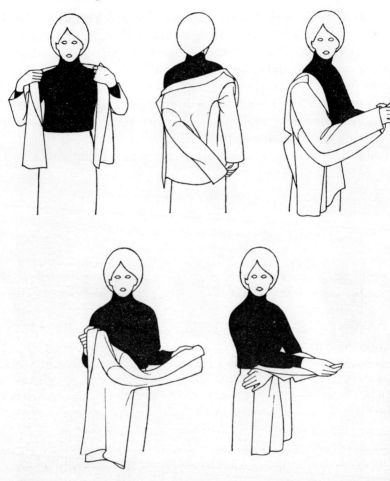

The model way of shedding a jacket can also save embarrassment in a restaurant

and fold the coat over your left arm, leaving your right hand free to show off a pocket, say.

Flaunting a fur

Fur coats may be heavier, but they're much easier to slip off. Instead of beginning by slipping the coat only slightly off your shoulders, you actually let it slide off completely, catching it with the crooks of your arms. Then straightening your arms, turn your palms upwards to catch the coat deftly by

Skill, cheerfulness and rhythm bring the 'electricity' to a fashion show

the collar as it drops to the ground. Move your right hand along to the middle of the collar, let go the left, and simply drag the coat behind you with all the nonchalance in the world. You can also slip off a bolero or a waistcoat like this, trailing it at your side as you go.

Draping a cape

Capes are the simplest of all to fling around your shoulders and models have enormous fun making flamboyant features of twirling them about, toreador-style, on the catwalk. You can also give huge scarves or shawls the same treatment.

With the lining of the cape away from you, grip the collar with your left-hand palm towards you and your right, a little further along, palm away. Swing the cape over your left shoulder, bringing your right arm over your head until the cape sits exactly on your shoulders, with your hands both on their respective sides, to take the cape off again, with your right hand gripping the collar, peel it off your right, then left shoulder, bringing your right arm behind your head, so the cape comes off, lining to the front. Quickly close the cape over to hide the lining and fold it over your left arm.

13
Job Possibilities

When you're confronted with the sheer variety of model work, you will appreciate how versatile a successful girl has to be. Modelling isn't just a case of 'sitting pretty'. One day you could be boxed in polystyrene on a studio set, while the photographer focuses on your perfectly painted lips, and the next, hang-gliding with a champagne glass in your hand. A model's life is full of surprises—that's why you have to be adaptable to survive. But at least with so many new faces, locations and situations to contend with, there's little chance of your becoming bored.

It's your career

Having said that you must learn to adapt, it must also be said that you don't *have* to do anything that you don't really want to—within reason. Your agency will discuss with you your particular specialities which you may want to stress on your card. Good teeth, legs, hands and hair all mean that you can—and will—subject them to scrutiny. (Some models work with hands or legs only, but they have to be exquisite and the work is obviously too limited to make it more than a possible part-time career.)

Your hobbies and proficiencies in other areas count also; you may roller skate, for example, swim, practise yoga, horseride, speak fluent French—even eat fire! You'd be surprised how everything comes in useful, especially for advertising work.

Nude work

Niggling doubts always surround the question of nude work. There are four basic categories which directly involve your body:

Corsetry means you have a figure particularly suited to showing off undergarments, like full and half-slips, bras, girdles, tights and stockings, or swimwear. This work involves anything from a thermal underwear catalogue to a full-colour spread of French silk underwear for a fashion magazine.

Semi-nude generally means the top half only (unless you're a leg girl). You're baring your breasts to illustrate health and beauty articles or to act as a background to an advertisement. You may or may not have to show your face as well.

Full nude work is similar in nature to semi-nude, except obviously there's more of you on show. Again the work can be strictly in 'good taste'.

'Glamour' modelling, which most fashion models secretly (or openly) despise, is the kind of work you see in 'men only' magazines—hard or soft pornography. Obviously, this type of work is extremely specialised and the models belong to specialist agencies.

Whether or not you do any type of work like this—even corsetry—is entirely up to you. As you'd imagine, there are special rates for 'body' shots such as these, and your agency will, or should, protect you from any work which may be unsavoury. (They usually have a blacklist of clients to avoid.) If a situation occurs on a photo-session which you feel uneasy about, don't argue with the client—go away and 'phone your agency immediately.

If, however, you ask my advice, or even my opinion, I would not want any young friend of mine to partake in any of the last three categories and I would not allow her—if I had some influence—to be associated with so-called 'glamour' modelling.

Editorial work

Editorial work consists largely of photography for magazines and newspapers. It's often the most creative and varied work, as the magazine industry especially is constantly trying to produce new or avant-garde slants to glamorous fashion and beauty themes. It is this work which provides you with the majority of printed matter for your portfolio. So the better your pictures, the more work you will attract with them.

Beauty work requires exquisitely clear skin and good features since a great proportion is very detailed indeed. The younger the skin the better, so models past twenty-five no longer model for beauty shots. Fashion work is more flexible as the total look is much more taken into consideration.

Advertising work

Advertising covers anything which is designed to sell a product or idea to the public and differs from editorial in that the promoter *pays* for his work to appear in the press, etc. As far as you are concerned, you could be posing for a photograph which will appear as a magazine or newspaper advertisement, a showcard for a cosmetics display, on a package for a shampoo, say, or a full-sized poster.

Catalogue and brochure work is the mainstay of many a model's income as most girls build up a regular clientèle and most mail order, fashion and cosmetic companies produce at least two catalogues annually, which account for a good few well-paid weeks' work. It's advertising which provides most of the travel, as a large proportion of catalogues and 'fantasy' advertisements are shot on location.

Promotion work

Promotion differs from advertising slightly, because although the work is used to promote a product, it is generally distributed to the trade or to the press as opposed to immediate public release. For example, a public relations company handling a fashion account may wish to prepare a series of photographs to send out to the press. These may simply be filed for reference or printed in magazines and newspapers who then usually credit the fashion company. This is really, then, a form of 'free' advertising which bridges the gap between pure editorial and full-scale advertising.

A notable exception to the 'promotion' rule, as far as you're concerned, is when you agree to become a 'house model' for a hairdressing salon. As I have already explained in an earlier chapter most salons have an agreement with their models. You get free hairdressing to a high standard (and with the mounting costs of colour and other processes, it's worth having). In return, you model for promotional pictures, videos, etc., and take part in shows and conferences, without charging them a fee, or at least, your full fee.

Show modelling

Show modelling is a major part of modelling. Some girls are able to alternate catwalk or ramp modelling with photographic assignments and in your early days, under your agent's guidance, you should be ready for either, or both. However, they are different arts. Photographic is more highly paid and claims the majority but many scores of magnificent and lovely girls find the excitement of the catwalk rewarding enough as well as being wholly engrossing. Applause is heady stuff and there is an indescribable thrill—a *frisson* that runs through a whole salon, from the audience and the press to the models and the dressers—when a new style emerges or a new designer triumphs.

The big fashion shows are usually held for about a fortnight twice a year in Paris, Italy and London when the top designers 'show' their collections to the buyers and press. As shows these days are much more choreographed, they require experienced girls who are able to adapt quickly to the dance-style of the catwalk.

House modelling

House modelling is different; the girl models a collection 'in house' for a season (between six to ten weeks, in the spring and autumn). Although it guarantees a steady income for a longish period, this work lacks the atmosphere and excitement of show work and is usually done by new girls wishing to gain experience and boost their finances. But there are of course house models who stay loyal for years to their bosses, models on whom the clothes are virtually designed and made, who indeed almost *become* 'the house'.

Mannequin modelling

Mannequin modelling is perhaps the strangest work of all. The dummies you see in shop windows are actually based on live models, who pose for the original casts. As modern dummies are made with fully articulated limbs, so that they appear as lifelike and natural as possible, modelling for them involves a variety of positions (sitting, standing, walking, etc.). It's like 'sitting' for a sculpture, with a difference. The results are certainly eerie when you see yourself in a shop window!

What will you be paid?

It's extremely difficult to be exact about modelling fees, as rates fluctuate according to the job and the client.

Editorial jobs are the least lucrative—the more prestigious the magazine, often the less lucre you'll get. But the prestige itself often leads to other work and you do have some good pictures for your book. **Advertising** pays up to £400 a day, roughly double the editorial rate, and sometimes carries an added bonus in the form of 'repeats'—royalties on film commercial work (for TV and cinema) and packages (hair colorants, cosmetics), depending on how widely exposed you and your work will be. The rate for **promotional** or **public relations** work falls somewhere in between. **Show-work** is paid by the hour or the day, varying from £40 to £100 a day and more. But in the case of block booking (like editorial or advertising trips abroad, or long 'seasons', etc.) to cover the entire period, the client usually negotiates a flat fee with your agency.

Never discuss fees with the client yourself. You should be 'above' that kind of thing—if only because your agent, who has more gall, is likely to get a bigger fee out of a client than modest little you. Making any kind of arrangement behind your agent's back may also be undermining work done in your best interests and gives rise to confusion. You could get 'double-booked'—i.e. booked both by you yourself and by the agency for the same day but for different jobs—and girls can get lynched for that, or at least dismissed by the agency.

Provincial modelling

Work for girls in the UK who live far from the capital cannot offer the same prestige or the same rewards as London does. I would estimate that at least 95 per cent of British modelling is centred on London and before any young hopeful embarks on this career in any other British town she or her advisers should first do some intelligent research.

The local Chamber of Commerce and local Job Centres may be useful, but perhaps not as useful as some local common sense. Read the classified advertisements—not for announcements by so-called model schools or money-seeking photographers offering portfolios, but to see how many real jobs there are for models offered in the situations vacant columns. Telephone the personnel officer of your local fashion houses and department stores, ask the advertising agencies and talk or write to the beauty and fashion editors of your local papers.

In some provincial towns in the UK, modelling is often combined with 'merchandising', i.e. arranging the display of your client's goods in the shops, or promotion work at major industrial exhibitions, e.g. helping to 'man' a stand, or handing out samples at big social or business functions.

Sensible models in the provinces, unless full bookings render them immune, often fill the leaner weeks (or months) with temporary secretarial or reception work while still keeping in regular touch with their agents. So scan the *whole* horizon before you embark. But, as in London, be tall and beautiful before you even think about it. And wherever you are it's a very good idea to have a second string to your bow, and indeed a second bow, such as training to be a secretary, a hospital worker, a receptionist or whatever you fancy, as long as it's a career that offers a measure of security, just in case.

14
This is How it is

I hope that so far I have been as helpful to those girls who want the attractiveness and the elegance of the legendary model without the actual work, as I have been to the intending models themselves. By now the latter know something of the measurements required, the discipline and the techniques. But before they finally decide whether they *can* face tackling the extreme highs and lows they should take one last look at the business through the eyes of model girls themselves and let these experiences help them make their final choice.

Louise

Louise is seventeen and has been in the business a mere six months. Some things came as quite a shock to her.

'I was terrified at first. Everyone seemed so ultra-trendy and flash and for three months I hated it. I felt terribly uncomfortable and shy. Straight from drama college, I just didn't know what to do. I wish I'd trained at model school but I hadn't—my only experience was from watching other models working and doing tests. The camera was so different from acting on stage. In front of the camera you have to be elegant! My parents helped me when I was spending out on model equipment and on my cards and I was still waiting to be paid. But I was very lucky—I got my first job (for a newspaper) from my very first casting. Everyone was kind to me, but I hated the clothes—they were so tarty!

'I still didn't join an agency. But in the end, when the work began to come through, I had to leave college. Besides, I think

Joanna Lumley, a Lucie Clayton graduate, is among the top British models in television commercials. Photo by John Adriaan

eventually I may go back to college, and modelling will have given me more insight into the drama and photography side. But for the moment the money is fantastic. I'm twenty times better off now than at college. And it *has* made me less self-conscious in a funny sort of way. People are a lot more casual about your looks than I thought they'd be. I don't panic so much about spots now, because I know I can cover them.

'Sometimes you really are treated like an object. I know that you're not booked for yourself—just your looks. But it still makes me niggly, even though I'm gradually getting used to it. I don't feel as upset as I used to. I've just learned to handle it better now.'

Annabel

At twenty-three, Annabel is what is normally considered a late starter. With only two months' modelling experience under her belt her story is quite exceptional.

A secretary at an advertising agency, she was 'discovered' by the make-up artist and photographer when she went to watch a photographic session for the cosmetic company her firm dealt with. Eventually, they used her in the commercial. Still, she had problems joining a model agency—she's only 5′ 6½″ (169 cm) tall. But they did reluctantly take her on after seeing her photographs. Although her biggest regret is that she can never do fashion work, Annabel has learned to take the rough with a pinch of philosophy.

'Modelling is much harder work than the job I was doing before. All that trailing around London on buses, seeing people who don't really take much notice of your book. The money, when it comes through, is marvellous. After two months' modelling I've already earned over half my old salary for the year. The other week I earned a couple of months' salary in a single day. But I'm still overdrawn.

'Your overheads are quite high: you have to pay for your tests to be printed and mounted up and you have to keep up appearances and spend a fortune on hair and skin products. Then there are the fares and all that shoe leather. On average, I spend around £5 per day—and that's not on taxis. Most models live at home when they start but I already had my flat. The ideal thing is to save around £500 to tide you over until the cheques come through. I'm just getting paid now for work I did when I started. But there's still the commission, VAT *on* the commission and income tax to pay from what's left.

'I said when I started I'd give it three months. But it's definitely worked out for me. Everyone loves a new face so I have to remind myself it isn't just my personal merit that gets me work. But it doesn't pay to think too much about that. The most important thing is not to take criticism too seriously. When they say things like "God, your eyes are really deep-set!" you could have so many complexes. Really, they're not insulting you—they're making a professional observation on the services you're offering. So you have to be quite dispassionate about yourself. On the other hand, some people become obsessed with themselves. They think they look like their pictures. They forget they've had a make-up artist working on them for two hours. And that's incredibly sad.'

Michele

Michele is a well-known show model, trained and launched on her career by Lucie Clayton Model School.

'My very first job was for Gucci. Several of us had to pose in the Bond Street boutique window, pretending we were dummies. Then, everytime someone walked past—we'd move. You can imagine how arresting that was! Seasons, though, are boring as hell. I did nine weeks for Cojana, trotting around in the same clothes, doing the same turns and flashing the same smiles four times a day. They paid us quite well, but we really had to work hard. My ankles used to swell because of constantly turning in the same direction.

'Shows are the best fun. My first ones were for top designers like Bill Gibb and Gina Fratini. John Bates actually flew a group of us to Paris in a private plane. There were some really superstar models over there—American and German girls—big names like Jerry Hall and Marie Helvin are today. I really felt I'd made it then. All the press were snapping away from behind the rails. We always had a day's rehearsal to learn the routine and work our walk out with our partners. Really, it was all a big laugh—everyone was so friendly.

'Shows today, though, aren't such a big thing, especially in England, where it's relatively low-key. The best are the art college shows because the clothes are always so much more adventurous and the students are so enthusiastic and friendly. A far cry from some of the top designers who get so fraught and fuss so much, you think they're going to kick you. But Paris shows are the ones with the electricity. First, there's the tension build-up, with hairdressers going mad, spray everywhere, and you screaming at the dresser because she's done the zip up the wrong way. Usually everyone drinks lots of wine to loosen up before going on—and you nearly *run* down the catwalk. Then there are the designers themselves. Some of them are so nervous, they daren't come out from behind the rails for the applause and have to be dragged on at the end. But you get a tremendous kick from the instant appreciation of the cheers and clapping at the end. And it's always exciting if you like the collection and you're the first to wear it in public. It *is* important to like the clothes, though. If you feel good, you look good. It all comes from inside. If you don't like the clothes, then you *have* to look good. And that's being plain professional.'

Agatha

Nineteen-year-old Agatha by contrast isn't sure that modelling is the right profession for her. Introduced to a model agency via one of its talent scouts visiting the north country, she left school and came down to London to test with a top photographer. The pictures were fine but after a few months things began to go sour. Eighteen months later, and both she and her agency are wondering whether it's really worth her while to carry on.

'I just loathe being scrutinised by other people and talked about as if I weren't there. They don't care how you feel—they know you're a model so they don't bother to conceal their criticisms or allow for the fact you may have feelings underneath it all. I've never been able to accept that I'm just an object, although practice has taught me to switch off. But sometimes I have to really force myself. At first it was soul destroying—I'd go home in tears, or wonder if I'd ever survive the session.

'My agency constantly criticises me for my attitude. They say I treat modelling as a hobby—I laze around and don't bother to promote myself. They are absolutely right. I dislike go-sees, though. You stand there like a prize cow and if they don't comment on your book you've no idea what they're thinking. But the money *is* good and the lifestyle can be quite relaxing—you've time to do what you want when you're not actually working. I know I don't really appreciate it but incredible though it may seem, it has broadened my outlook and taught me self-control.'

Clare

Someone else with mixed feelings is twenty-five-year-old Clare. Originally a dancer, five years ago she won the Vogue model competition and began a successful new career. But now her thoughts are leaning towards a future as a photographer and she has already had two exhibitions and is preparing a book of her work.

'My first impression of the modelling business was that there were no real answers to my questions. Everyone had different views, which made me very apprehensive.

'What annoys me about this business is the people. There's always a prima donna—it could be the make-up artist, the client or the model herself. But I believe firmly that everyone should be equal "on session". If you start causing a scene then it's obvious you just like drawing attention to yourself and that makes life very difficult. It's tough, but sometimes you have to accept that you're a lump of meat. You're there because your face fits.

'But modelling does have its rewards. You can work anywhere in the world. What other job allows you to just fly out and carry on?

'On the other hand, you can lose control. It can be a terribly destructive business because it's a fantasy world. The most dangerous time is in your first year when you're entering a situation which gives you the opportunity to do things you never did before, like go to clubs, date attractive men and have the cash to waste on drugs. The so-called glamour side is the one that can be the most dangerous. People lose perspective of how mundane life really is. You *must* keep aware of real life—it's so easy to forget!'

Amanda

Amanda's gentle personality and down-to-earth good sense are two great assets which have guided her through a happy and successful career of ten years' standing. She started out after a course at the Lucie Clayton Model School. A serene beauty, she isn't bored yet!

'When I joined the course I didn't know a thing about modelling. I lived out of London and the nearest I'd come to a photographic session was my weekly magazine. I gained so much confidence at the School, including poise, deportment—really they taught me how to behave!

'When I began working, I felt totally overwhelmed—completely out of my depth. I'd hear all the other girls talking about their boyfriends with yachts and colour TV's and couldn't believe things like that actually happened. It was a bit like living in a movie. Everything seemed larger than life.

'My very first interview was a nightmare, though. I went to see someone on a big "glossy" and all she did was flick through my book, whilst still on the phone! Then she handed it back to me without zipping it up again and all the pictures fell out. I was mortified—I went home in floods of tears. Not everyone was that bad—but you always meet someone you're never quite able to forgive!

'The hardest thing about modelling is getting your "marbles" together. I've seen so many girls who think it's all they've got in their life. We call them models' models—they forget they've a home life. Because they're models, they think they are special—they don't realise everyone's special no matter what they do! People are very nice to you when you're on top but if you're not it's a different story.

'Sometimes it's hard to tell who your true friends are in this business. A calm home life matters so much. It's terribly important the way you're brought up. I've seen young kids of around fifteen or sixteen, with maybe not quite such stable backgrounds, who've become totally ruined by it all. You must learn to adopt a fairly sensible attitude especially on trips, say, when you really are living off your wits and there's no one to help you. It's all very nice to go to these places like Milan, for example. But with playboys hanging around the hotels day and night, you can get yourself into a real mess. I just sit in my hotel room and knit!

'When you start, don't take everything too seriously. Modelling takes discipline and perseverance—you must have a realistic attitude to the people you're working with. You're paid a lot of money for what you're doing so it's up to you to do your best. It's not enough to turn up late with chewed nails and without so much as a pair of tights or flesh-coloured bra. That's not *trying*. But do take care of yourself. Save a little money and spend a little. Don't save the lot for a rainy day—enjoy it. You're only young once and you might as well get something out of it. It's a fantastic time, but just try and be sensible.'

And for me that's just the right note to end on. Enjoy yourself, be sensible and take care!

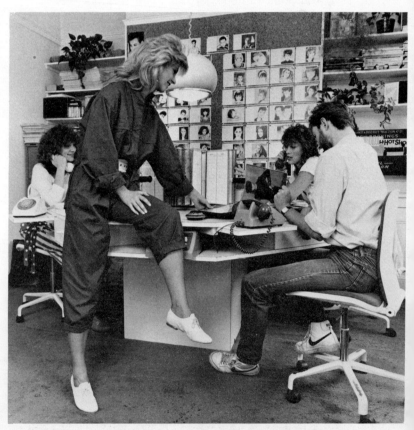

Taking bookings at Premier Model Agency, one of the busiest in London

Appendix 1
Nutrients

For those of you who, having read and digested the dietary details in Chapter 6, are interested in the more intricate breakdown of the nutrients and their precise functions in the body, below is the fascinating story of how our diet really makes us tick.

Protein—the building bricks

Protein is the stuff of which life itself is made. The body tissue is largely protein and so needs daily supplies for reinforcement, growth and repair.

Protein itself is composed of smaller units called **amino acids**, which bond together in chains to determine the nature of each particular type of protein. Not every type of body tissue needs the same kind (brain tissue, for example, differs from blood) so the proteins are broken down into their amino acids by the digestive system and dispatched by the blood to the appropriate regions.

There are over twenty amino acids, eight of which are vital for healthy adult life. Eating combinations of proteins (bread and cheese, for example, or beans on toast) will ensure you get an adequate supply of all the amino acid types.

An adult woman needs around fifty grams of protein daily. The best known forms of protein are animal—fish, meat (especially liver) chicken, eggs, cheese and other dairy products are undoubtedly the best-value sources. But pulses like lentils, soya beans, red kidney beans, peas as well as cereal products like bread and nuts, all contain significant amounts and are lower in fat.

Carbohydrates—the energisers

Carbohydrates fall into two groups. 'Available' carbohydrates comprise sugars (derived mostly from sugar or glucose and in much smaller amounts from fruit and milk as fructose and lactose) and starch (from cereals, like wheat, rice and vegetables). Unavailable carbohydrates like celluloses and pectin from vegetables and fruit have no nutritional value, but are important roughage, or fibre.

The main function of carbohydrates is to supply the body with simple sugar, or energy, in more sophisticated chemical units called **monosaccharides**, and again different foods contain different values. In the starch group many monosaccharides link together to form **polysaccharides**, which the digestive system has to break down into the original mono form before conversion to glucose. Glucose is then carried to all parts of the body, and stored in the muscles and liver to provide a constant supply of energy. During intense physical activity, the glucose is broken down to provide heat and energy necessary for the task.

Although undeniably part of a major carbohydrate group, sugar has no other nutritional properties and is, in fact, completely unnecessary in a healthy diet. The body is perfectly able to derive all its glucose from the starch group and it is usually our 'sweet tooth' which tips the balance of our body's needs. So distrust sweets, biscuits, sweet fruit or soft drinks and alcohols.

Fats—energy, but handle with caution!

Fat is the richest dietary source of energy, yielding more units (or calories) weight for weight than carbohydrates or protein. But as it is so phenomenally high in energy units, you need relatively low proportions. If you consume more than your body can use, fat is stored in the body, causing weight gain, and in severe cases heart and circulatory problems. Fats are composed of fatty acids which band together with other chemicals (like glycerine). As there are forty different types of fatty acids, the variety of fats is considerable.

Doctors now say that the more desirable fats are of non-animal origin (olive oil, for example, and ground-nut, soya or sunflower oil) as they are low in the saturated fatty acids which raise the fat levels in the blood. But ideally all fats should be limited.

Grilling, steaming or braising foods, especially those already containing fats, like meat, eliminates the need to add more in cooking. A limited intake of dairy products like milk, butter, hard cheese, eggs, trimming the visible fat off meat and favouring low fat high protein foods like cottage cheese, fish, pulses and substituting low-fat yoghurt for cream or fruits and skimmed milk for whole should regulate your intake. Watch too for 'hidden' fats. Nuts contain a high proportion of oil, albeit vegetable, whilst cakes, biscuits and pastries, especially 'puff' or 'flaky', contain a fair bit. Fried foods are definitely dangerous!

Minerals—the back-up system

Minerals are vital components of the skeletal system, body cells and the fluids which hold the body together. There are over nineteen present in the body; the major elements are as follows:

Calcium helps build bones and teeth, is necessary for the normal clotting of blood and the maintenance of the nervous and muscular tissue. Growing children and nursing mothers need calcium the most, as a deficiency can cause poor teeth and bones, especially in children. Good calcium sources are primarily dairy products, as are fish eaten with the bones, nuts, pulses and bread. Vegetables also contain small amounts.

Phosphorus is needed along with calcium for healthy bones and teeth, as well as playing a vital role in the composition of body fluids. As it is found in almost all foods it's unlikely you'll suffer from a deficiency.

Sodium and chlorine—the compound constituents of salt—are necessary to maintain the correct balance of fluid between the cells and tissues and the levels of acid in the body. All body fluids contain just under 1 per cent of salt. It is lost through perspiration and urine and a severe lack of it causes dehydration and cramps. (Hence the need for salt tablets in very hot countries.) An excess, however, is thought to be a contributory factor to high blood pressure. So again, moderate your intake.

A good first step is to leave the salt off the table, as most cooked foods already contain a fair proportion of salt. Restricting the amount you sprinkle on vegetables to a pinch should give just enough flavour without overloading your system. Salty foods to watch out for are bacon, ham, salted and smoked fish (kippers, smoked herrings, etc.) canned meats and crisps. Restrict your additional salt to other foods if you eat any of these. Pastry also has a certain amount of 'hidden' salt.

Potassium works with sodium to maintain the correct fluid balance in the body, and is found in a wide variety of foods, so deficiencies are rare.

Iron is one of the most important minerals, as it is vital for the formation of haemoglobin, the red pigment in blood which carries oxygen to every part of the body, and carbon dioxide away from it. When a corpuscle breaks down (after around six weeks) the iron is salvaged and used to form fresh corpuscles in the bone marrow. In spite of this recycling process, deficiencies in iron can occur through loss of blood (women are especially at risk, with long or heavy periods) and anaemia can result. The body can also regulate how much iron is absorbed from food; if its stores are low, its absorption rate increases and vice versa.

Foods high in iron are liver, red meat, wholemeal bread, herrings, raisins, eggs and dried fruit, as well as dark green leafy vegetables like watercress.

Iodine is needed to form the hormone which the thyroid gland secretes in order to regulate the metabolic rate, or the rate at which energy is used to maintain the body processes. Iodine is usually quite rich in the soil, and so vegetables absorb certain proportions. The richest source, however, is the sea. (Seaweed is extremely high in iodine, if you can stomach it!) Seafood is probably a homelier option.

Fluoride is needed to form the enamel on teeth and so fight against tooth decay. Many area health authorities add it to the water and it is also available in toothpaste. Tea contains a certain amount.

Magnesium, with phosphorus, helps build healthy bones and teeth and is found in a wide variety of foods. Deficiencies are rare.

Copper is needed to help iron form red blood cells, as is **cobalt**. This is contained in the vitamin B_{12}—a deficiency of which is also a major cause of anaemia.

Trace elements account for the remaining minerals each needed in minute proportions, but which nevertheless play an important role in the body. A good diet contains all of them, so again, deficiences are rare.

Vitamins—the infection fighters

Vitamins are organic elements which the body needs to maintain its integrity, fight infection and disease. As mentioned, vitamins often depend on each other in order to function, but their relationship literally hangs in the balance. A deficiency of one, or an overdose of a vitamin which the body does not automatically dispose of, can hamper the smooth functioning of the partnership. For this reason, it is unwise to take single vitamins in high-dosage pill form unless you (or your doctor) are sure you are deficient. A healthy balanced diet should supply you with all the vitamins you need, in realistic proportions. If you feel you must take vitamin pills, take them in multivitamin form, where the proportions have been calculated for you.

Vitamins fall into two groups; fat-soluble and water-soluble. The **fat-soluble vitamins** are quite hardy and heat-resistant, so cooking does little to damage them. These are vitamins A, D, E and K. **Water-soluble vitamins** (the B group and C) have to be handled a little more carefully. Foods containing these which are overcooked in water or even exposed to air for long periods, can diminish their content. Vegetables, therefore, are best baked or steamed whole, with their skins on where possible and not shredded or chopped. Eating them fresh from the ground is obviously of enormous advantage, but not always possible for city dwellers like models, and budding business women. Nevertheless, avoid wilted-looking vegetables, and where good fresh supplies look scarce opt instead for frozen vegetables. They're a better bet than unfresh 'fresh' ones!

Vitamin A, or retinol, is an important vitamin with many functions. It maintains the mucous membranes and forms part of the pigment in the retina which allows you to see in dim lighting. It also plays a part in developing the tooth enamel and dentine as well as contributing to the overall normal growth of the body. Deficiences cause a lowered resistance to infection, a dry rough skin and thickly coated throat and blocked nose. Vision—particularly in the dark—becomes affected. An overdose, though is more likely and can be dangerous.

The body stores vitamin A in the liver, as retinol, so two or three meals per week with a good supply is sufficient. Vitamin boosts such as halibut liver oil can tip the balance. Foods rich in vitamin A are liver (because all animals store it in the liver) fish and fish oil, margarine to which it has been added, butter, cheese and eggs.

As **carotene** (which the body converts to retinol) it is found in dark green leafy plants such as spinach and watercress and carrots (hence the old myth that they can make you see in the dark!). To a lesser extent it is also found in cabbage and peas.

The B vitamins. This 'complex' of vitamins is often found together in the same foods although there are some exceptions. The body cannot store them for long periods, so that as they are such an important group especially involved in the metabolic process, and nervous system, they need to be taken daily.

Vitamin B_1 (thiamin) helps to release a steady amount of energy from carbohydrates. The more carbohydrates you eat, the more vitamin B_1 you need. In a good diet deficiencies are rare, but when they do occur can cause depression, listlessness, constipation, indigestion and nausea. Excesses are lost in urine. Good sources are pork and pork products, milk and vegetables. B_1 also contributes to the health of the brain, nerves and heart muscle.

Vitamin B_2 (riboflavin) is also concerned in the metabolism of carbohydrates for the respiration of tissues and for healthy skin, hair and nails. Dairy products are the prime source, as well as white meat, liver, kidneys, cereals, eggs and vegetables. Deficiences are rare, as this vitamin is found in such a wide range of regularly eaten foods, but they can cause cracking and scaling of the skin. A cautionary note: *milk exposed to light loses 10 per cent of its B_2 content per hour*! So bring it in from the doorstep.

Nicotinic acid (niacin) joins with the first two B vitamins to metabolise carbohydrates and is also needed for the maintenance of the gastrointestinal tract, the skin and the nervous tissue. It is found mainly in red meats, especially liver (vegetarians can keep their quota up with Marmite), as well as wholemeal bread, and peanuts to a lesser extent. Deficiencies—again rare—can cause skin problems, depression and fatigue.

Vitamin B_3 (pantothenic acid) helps fight infection by building antibodies. It is found in beans, cereals and liver and is rarely seriously deficient.

Vitamin B_6 (pyridoxine) is needed to metabolise amino acids, so therefore quantities needed are linked directly with the amount of protein consumed. It is found in protein foods: milk, fish, meat and cereals. Deficiency in humans is virtually unknown.

Folic acid helps prevent anaemia by contributing to healthy blood cells. It is found in yeast and dark green leafy vegetables, and a variety of other foods common to the B group. Deficiencies are unlikely, although pregnant women are sometimes given a booster course.

Vitamin B$_{12}$ (cyanocobalamin) is needed for the production of healthy blood cells and the prevention of anaemia. It is found only in 'animal' foods like milk, eggs, fish and liver, so deficiencies can occur from following a particularly stringent slimming or, more dangerous, a vegetarian diet which excludes all animal elements. For this reason, it may be a good idea to consult your doctor before embarking on any drastic change of diet for a substantial period of time.

Vitamin C (ascorbic acid) is probably the best known of all the vitamins, thanks to its reputation of being able to prevent and cure the common cold. Although some experts say that vitamin C has only a placebo, or 'psychological', effect, it does play a part in keeping the mucous membranes healthy and building a resistance to infection, as well as contributing to healthy skin and gums and healing wounds. But whether it is the 'wonder cold cure' is still debatable, and massive doses of it can lead to kidney stones and affect the bones.

It is an extremely fragile vitamin, easily destroyed by heat, light, air and damage like bruising and cutting. So vegetables should be cooked for the least possible time in the minimum of water or preferably eaten raw. Foods high in vitamin C are, of course, citrus fruits—like oranges, lemons, limes and grapefruits—blackcurrants and, to a lesser degree, green leafy vegetables like mustard and cress, cabbage, lettuce, Brussels sprouts and potatoes and tomatoes.

Vitamin D (cholecalciferol). This is the only vitamin that the body actually manufactures for itself, and so doesn't have to be eaten. The action of ultraviolet light on the pigment in the skin stimulates production. You don't have to lie in the sun for hours, or indeed develop a tan. Normal year-round exposure is usually sufficient, unless you swathe all your limbs in clothes all year round. You need vitamin D to help the body absorb calcium and phosphorus, to build and maintain healthy bones, the mineral content of which is constantly being renewed.

Fish high in fat—like sardines, pilchards, herrings and salmon, and especially cod liver oil—are natural sources high in vitamin D. Look out also for margarines to which vitamins A and D have been added. Some local authorities (especially in the north of England and Scotland) add vitamin D to milk. As it can be stored in the liver, one meal a week of vitamin D-rich foods is sufficient, plus your normal quota of sunshine.

Vitamin E (tocopherols). Don't believe that this is the 'wonder' vitamin for long life, vitality and a better than ever sex life. Sorry, but that's just 'health store' jargon. Although it is an integral part of our diet, experts have not yet 'cracked' exactly why, as deficiencies in humans are unknown. It is mostly found in grains and cereals.

Vitamin K is vital for wound-healing and blood-clotting. You can find it in liver, green leafy vegetables and tomatoes, but the natural bacteria inside the human intestines also manufacture it, so that deficiencies in adults are rare.

Water

Although water has no nutritional value, it is absolutely vital in our diet. Almost two thirds of our body weight is taken up by water and dehydration is one of the greatest threats to us. We can survive for weeks without food, but without water it would all be over in a matter of days.

We need on average around three to five pints of water daily, depending on how hot the weather is or how much fluid we lose through exertion and perspiration. We can't normally drink too much water: the kidneys neatly dispose of any excess, through our frequent trips to the loo! Our body tells us if we need more—we simply feel thirsty. Although our daily intake does not necessarily need to be pure water (coffee, tea, fruit juice, etc., are of course all water-based), beware drinks containing hidden calories. If in doubt, drink ordinary tap or mineral water. The carbonated variety is delicious with a slice of lemon or lime.

Fibre

Humans cannot digest certain plant components, but whereas fibre does not supply us with nutrition, it plays an extremely important role in our diet by binding the other waste products together and making their elimination from the bowels more efficient. Constipation (i.e. a delay in your personal regular pattern of bowel action—you do not, in fact, *have* to 'go' every day) can be averted by sufficient fibre in your diet. It should be totally unnecessary to resort to unnatural laxatives, and is in fact dangerous to take them regularly. Pot bellies are safely cured by a healthy diet and exercise, not pills! Good sources of fibre are bran, wheat and husk, wholemeal cereals, pastas, breads, fruit and vegetables (especially raw).

Appendix 2
Advanced make-up

If you've followed the make-up advice in Chapter 11, feel at home with your everyday make-up and want to advance your technique to more professional levels, the following notes are guidelines on make-up for catwalk and camera.

Model make-up

Making up for the camera and catwalk relies on the same basic principles which you follow for a natural, everyday look. But even for the most natural, outdoor-look pictures, the techniques are slightly different.

Light is crucially important. Whereas a clear, natural make-up for daylight needs to be done in daylight itself—or under fluorescent lighting, the nearest to natural light—studio and catwalk lights have an entirely different effect on both your facial contours and the colours you use on them.

Basically, the kind of light from an ordinary light-bulb gives off a fair amount of orange, yellow and red; so if you're wearing those colours, they'll really stand out. Greens and blues, however, recede into the background (in fact in very dull lighting, it's virtually impossible to tell the difference between them, because the pigment just isn't picked up). Outside in natural daylight, the reverse occurs. Blues and greens fluoresce, whereas orange, pink and red don't look quite so bright. Studio make-up mirrors are invariably surrounded with a row of electric light bulbs (a hangover from stage make-up days), so you apply your photographic make-up accordingly.

The kind of lighting which photographers use, however, varies considerably, and can do a lot to flatter, or fight the make-up. (Most photographers take polaroid tests as a vague guide to how the final effect will look on the transparencies, so that make-up artists can adjust their work before the real shooting starts.) Some bulbs diffuse the light; flashes have the opposite effect. It's all a matter of experience, and knowing your photographer and his techniques! Overhead lighting (used especially for hair photography) emphasises your facial contours. Hollows will appear deeper and high spots will catch the light.

Use these steps below as a rough guideline to photographic colour and contour work:

(1) In front of the make-up mirror, analyse your face. Remember that as artificial light throws your features into relief, your use of colour and texture will be more extreme, emphasising with shading and reflective tones. Study your face from all angles. Whereas in normal circumstances your features are constantly moving, detracting or hiding irregularities and flaws, a photograph is *still*, concentrating on one aspect of your face only.

(2) Before the foundation stage, using cream products (like a dark and light make-up stick), correct flaws like heavy chins, weak jawlines, crooked nose, and sloping eyes. It's quite acceptable to use fairly deep shading (especially for black and white photographs) because of the brightness of the lights. But blend well at the edges for a natural finish. As overhead lights always throw the eyes into shadow, blend a very light shade (or non-sparkly highlighter) all around the eye area, to avoid a tired, hollow look.

(3) Lightly sponging foundation over your basic shadow work helps both blend it in and look even more natural. Don't use too much, but gradually build it up until your face looks even-toned and well-covered. Set your foundation with plenty of translucent powder—your face should be *completely* matt. Any shine will immediately register as 'flare' under the lights. Powder diffuses and deflects light and gives an extra-even finish.

(4) Use powder blusher over your foundation and powder both to boost the effect of your underlying contour work and to give extra colour and vitality to your complexion. Dust highlighter powder on points which you want to stand out, like cheekbones and high on browbones, or on your chin if you feel it recedes. For very natural shots, you can do all your shading, highlighting *and* blusher work *over* foundation and powder, using powder products. But they still will not produce such a marked effect as your basic stick shapers, and are best used for colour photography only for this reason.

(5) Photographic eye make-up takes day make-up a stage further. Go to town on highlighting, shaping and shading, to make the eyes look more dramatic. Use your colours to shape and correct. Shape your brows to give more expression to your eyes (extending them at the temples make your eyes look wider, further apart). Remember to brush them through with a damp browbrush to de-clog them of foundation and moisturiser. Individual artificial lashes, far from looking heavy or false, can be really effective. Two or three added to the outer corners of the eyes open and make them look wider. Blend them into your natural lashes with mascara.

(6) Remember that as light drains colour, you'll need to choose a fairly bright lipstick. (Even 'no make-up' shots usually call for just a touch of gloss to bring out the strength of the natural lip colour). Correct your lip contour with a lip pencil. Plenty of gloss or highlighter on the centre of the lips adds fullness, whilst to minimise your lips blot for a more matt finish.

When making-up for the catwalk, you need to exaggerate *everything*. The sheer strength and whiteness of the lights bleaches out colour. On the other hand, it also flatters as it blocks out blemishes and evens the skin tone, so your concealing work isn't quite so important. Your skin should be absolutely matt—no trace of shine. (Plenty of powder also helps prevent the make-up melting under the heat of those very strong lights.) Put all the accent on your eyes, cheeks and lips. Models often go for very dramatic make-up winging right out at the temples, using powerful fluorescent colours. Intensely bright blusher makes an impact when swept high across the cheekbones and browbones, in two distinct parallel lines, disappearing into the hairline; or blend high on your cheekbones again, but take the colour round and up onto your temples like an exaggerated comma framing your eye structure. Lips are by necessity very strong, with plenty of gloss for the lights to pick up. Shimmering gold highlight also looks effective on cheek and browbones. Don't be afraid to go over the top with catwalk make-up—it's simply an impression you're creating, seen from a long way off.